THE COMMONWEALTH AND INTERNATIONAL LIBRARY
Joint Chairmen of the Honorary Editorial Advisory Board
SIR ROBERT ROBINSON, O.M., F.R.S., LONDON
DEAN ATHELSTAN SPILHAUS, MINNESOTA
Publisher: ROBERT MAXWELL, M.C., M.P.

RURAL AND ENVIRONMENTAL STUDIES DIVISION
General Editors: S. MCB. CARSON, R. W. COLTON

Introduction to Crop Husbandry

Introduction
to Crop Husbandry

BY

J. A. R. LOCKHART, B.Agr.(Dist.)

AND

A. J. L. WISEMAN, N.D.A., C.D.A.

ROYAL AGRICULTURAL COLLEGE, CIRENCESTER

PERGAMON PRESS

OXFORD . LONDON . EDINBURGH . NEW YORK
TORONTO . PARIS . BRAUNSCHWEIG

Pergamon Press Ltd., Headington Hill Hall, Oxford
4 & 5 Fitzroy Square, London W.1

Pergamon Press (Scotland) Ltd., 2 & 3 Teviot Place, Edinburgh 1

Pergamon Press Inc., 44–01 21st Street, Long Island City, New York 11101

Pergamon of Canada Ltd., 6 Adelaide Street East, Toronto, Ontario

Pergamon Press S.A.R.L., 24 rue des Ecoles, Paris 5e

Friedr. Vieweg & Sohn, Verlag, Postfach 185, 33 Braunschweig
West Germany

Printed in Great Britain by Dawson & Goodall Ltd., Bath

CONTENTS

FOREWORD

IN commending this book I would like to stress the importance of making the rudiments of agriculture available at Farm Institute and Day Release level. It is our technicians, our foremen and stockmen, as much as our farmers and farm managers, who will require intellectual assurance as well as intuitive skill if agriculture is to match in technological advance the manufacturing industries of the future. Agriculture has peculiar problems of its own which lie in the fields either of engineering, animal nutrition or agronomy. Mr. Lockhart and Mr. Wiseman have produced a book which deals comprehensively with the last category in a manner that should not be too advanced for the arable foreman of tomorrow. They give the subject a modern slant by incorporating such matters as the selective control of weeds, the principles of crop storage and field meteorology within the traditional framework of geology, botany and chemistry. In short they take much of the scientific mystery out of the subject by describing in basic terms those forces which promote and those factors which inhibit the growth of economic plants. This then is a grammar without which modern farming will not again become an art.

Whitehall Place, S.W.1.

JOHN GREEN
Chairman of the
Agricultural Advisory Council
for England and Wales

PREFACE

THIS book is an introduction to the science and practice of crop husbandry. It is written in simple language without losing its technical value. Young people doing their practical training will find it helpful for explaining modern farming practices of growing and harvesting crops. All aspects of the subject are dealt with, such as the growth and development of plants, types and management of soils, drainage and irrigation, modern practices of growing and harvesting crops, management of grassland—including conservation, typical life-cycles of common pests and diseases, and the latest developments in the use of chemicals as fertilizers and in the control of weeds, pests and diseases. Suggestions for classwork are also included at the end of sections.

Students taking the City and Guilds General Agriculture (Part 1) and similar examinations can use it as a textbook, and those taking higher examinations will find the book a valuable source of basic information which will be enlarged on in their courses.

The authors acknowledge with very grateful thanks the valuable help given by their wives in preparing and typing the manuscript.

J. A. R. LOCKHART
A. J. L. WISEMAN

INTRODUCTION

Crops are plants which have been carefully selected and developed to produce food for man and animals.

Crop husbandry is the practice of growing and harvesting crops. The main objective is to produce good crops as economically as possible without impoverishing the land.

The methods used have been developed over the past centuries from practical experience and experiments. In recent years there have been many sweeping changes as the result of:

(a) introduction of many new and improved varieties,
(b) better use of fertilizers,
(c) better control of pests and diseases,
(d) chemical weed control,
(e) rapid improvements in the mechanization of such operations as seed-bed preparation, planting, harvesting and storage.

An understanding of how plants grow, and what they need, is a useful guide when providing for their requirements.

Good crop husbandry is really good management of crop plants so that they are provided with the best possible conditions for growth.

CHAPTER I

PLANTS

What they Are; What they Do; and How they Live

Plants are living organisms consisting of innumerable tiny cells. They differ from animals in many ways but the most important difference is that plants can build up valuable organic substances from simple materials. The most important part of this building process is the production of *carbohydrates*—this is called *photosynthesis*.

PHOTOSYNTHESIS

In photosynthesis a special green substance called *chlorophyll* uses *light* energy (normally sunlight) to change *carbon dioxide* and *water* into *sugars* (carbohydrates) in the *green* parts of the plant. The daily amount of photosynthesis is limited by the duration and intensity of sunlight. The amount of carbon dioxide available is also a limiting factor. Shortage of water and low temperatures can also reduce photosynthesis.

The cells which contain chlorophyll also have yellow pigments such as *carotene*. Crop plants can only build up chlorophyll in the light and so any leaves which develop in the dark are yellow and cannot produce carbohydrates.

Oxygen is released during photosynthesis and the process may be set out as follows:

$$\text{Carbon dioxide} + \text{water} + \text{energy} \xrightarrow{\text{chlorophyll}} \text{carbohydrates} + \text{oxygen}$$

$$6CO_2 \qquad 6H_2O \qquad \underset{\text{rays)}}{\text{(sun's}} \quad \text{sunlight} \qquad C_6H_{12}O \qquad 6O_2$$

(glucose or fructose)

This process not only provides the basis for all our food but it also supplies the oxygen which animals and plants need for respiration.

The simple carbohydrates, such as *glucose*, may build up to form *starch* for storage purposes, or to *cellulose* for building cell walls. *Fats* and *oils* are formed from carbohydrates. *Protein* material, which is an essential part of all living cells, is made from carbohydrates and nitrogen compounds.

Most plants consist of *roots*, *stems*, *leaves* and *reproductive parts* and need *soil* in which to grow.

The *roots* spread through the spaces between the particles in the soil and anchor the plant. In a plant such as wheat the root system may total many miles.

The *leaves*, with their broad surfaces, are the main parts of the plant where photosynthesis occurs (see Fig. 1).

A very important feature of the leaf structure is the presence of large numbers of tiny pores (*stomata*) on the surface of the leaf (see Fig. 2). There are usually thousands of stomata per square inch of leaf surface. Each pore (stoma) is oval-shaped and surrounded by two guard cells. When the guard cells are turgid (full of water) the stoma is open and when they lose water the stoma closes.

The carbon dioxide used in photosynthesis *diffuses* into the leaf through the stomata and most of the water vapour leaving the plant, and the oxygen from photosynthesis diffuses out through the stomata.

TRANSPIRATION

The evaporation of water from plants is called *transpiration*. It mainly occurs through the stomata and has a cooling effect on the leaf cells. Water in the cells of the leaf can pass into the pore spaces in the leaf and then out through the stomata as water vapour (see Fig. 3).

The rate of transpiration varies considerably. It is greatest when the plant is well supplied with water and the air outside the leaf is warm and dry. In very hot or windy weather water evaporates from the guard cells and so the stomata close and reduce the rate of transpiration. The stomata also close in very cold weather (e.g. 32°F, 0°C).

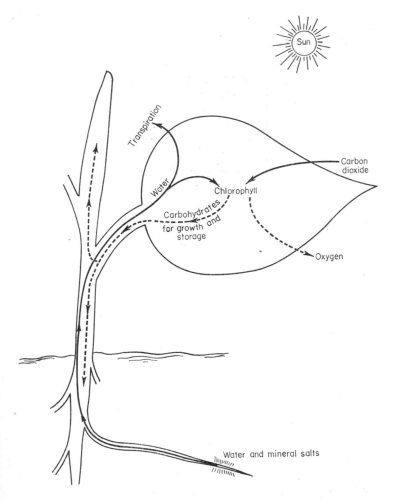

FIG. 1. Photosynthesis illustrated diagrammatically.

The rate of loss is reduced if the plant is short of water because the guard cells then lose water and close the stomata; it is also retarded if the humidity of the atmosphere is high.

The stomata guard cells close (and so transpiration ceases) during darkness. They close because photosynthesis ceases and water is lost from the guard cells (osmosis) when some of the sugars present change to starch.

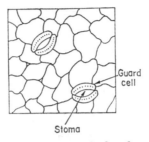

FIG. 2. Stomata on leaf surface.

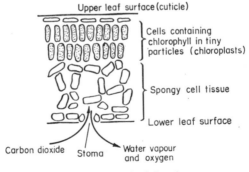

FIG. 3. Cross-section of a green leaf showing gaseous movements during daylight.

RESPIRATION

Plants, like animals, breathe, i.e. they take in oxygen which combines with organic foodstuffs and this releases energy, carbon dioxide and water. Farm crops are likely to be checked in growth if the roots are deprived of oxygen for respiration as might occur in a waterlogged soil.

TRANSLOCATION

The movement of materials through the plant is known as *translocation*.

The *xylem* or *wood vessels* which carry the water and mineral salts (*sap*) from the roots to the leaves are tubes made from dead cells. The cross walls of the cells have disappeared and the longitudinal walls are thickened with *lignum* to form wood. These tubes help to strengthen the stem.

The *phloem tubes* (*bast*) carry organic material through the plant, for example, sugars and amino acids from the leaves to storage parts or growing points. These vessels are chains of living cells, not lignified, and with cross walls which are perforated—hence the alternative name—*sieve tubes*.

In the stem the xylem and phloem tubes are usually found in a ring near the outside of the stem.

In the root, the xylem and phloem tubes form separate bundles and are found near the centre of the root.

UPTAKE OF WATER BY PLANTS

Water is taken into the plant from the soil. This occurs mainly through the root hairs near the root tip. There are thousands (perhaps millions) of root tips (and root hair regions) on a single healthy crop plant (see Fig. 4).

The absorption of water into the plant in this way is due to a suction pull which starts in the leaves. As water transpires (evaporates) from the cells in the leaf more water is drawn from the xylem tubes which extend from the leaves to the root tips. In these tubes the water is stretched like a taut wire or thread. This is possible because the tiny particles (molecules) of water hold together very firmly when in narrow tubes. The pull of this water in the xylem tubes of the root is transferred through the root cells to the root hairs and so water is absorbed into the roots and up to

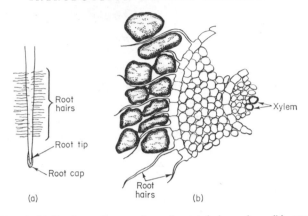

FIG. 4. (a) Section of root tip and root hair region, (b) cross-section of root showing the root hairs as tube-like elongations of the surface cells in contact with soil particles.

the leaves. In general, the greater the rate of transpiration, the greater is the amount of water taken into the plant. The rate of absorption is slowed down by:

(a) shortage of water in the soil,

(b) lack of oxygen for root respiration (e.g. in waterlogged soils),

(c) a high concentration of salts in the soil water near the roots.

Normally, the concentration of the soil solution does not interfere with water absorption. High soil water concentration can occur in salty soils and near bands of fertilizer. Too much fertilizer near developing seedlings may damage germination by restricting the uptake of water.

OSMOSIS

Much of the water movements into and from cell to cell in plants is due to *osmosis*. This is a process in which a solvent, such as water, will flow through a *semi-permeable* membrane (e.g. a cell wall) from a weak solution to a more concentrated one. The cellwall may allow only the water to pass through. The force exerted by such a flow is called the *osmotic pressure*. In plants, the normal movement of the water is into the cell. However, if the concentration of a solution outside the cell is greater than that inside, there is a loss of water from the cell, and its contents contract (shrivel); this is called *plasmolysis*.

UPTAKE OF NUTRIENTS

The absorption of chemical substances (nutrients) into the root cells is partly due to a *diffusion* process but it is mainly due to ability of the cells near root tips to *accumulate* such nutrients. The process is complicated and not fully understood. It is slowed up if root respiration is checked by a shortage of oxygen.

Plant Groups

Plants can be divided into annuals, biennials and perennials according to their total length of life.

ANNUALS

Typical examples are wheat, barley and oats which complete their life history in one growing season, i.e. starting from the seed, in 1 year they develop roots, stem and leaves and then produce flowers and seed before dying.

BIENNIALS

These plants grow for 2 years. They spend the first year in producing roots, stem and leaves, and the following year in producing the flowering stem and seeds, after which they die.

Sugar-beet, swedes and turnips are typical biennials, although the grower treats these crops as annuals, harvesting them at the end of the first year when all the foodstuff is stored up in the root.

PERENNIALS

They live for more than 2 years and, once fully developed, they usually produce seeds each year. Many of the grasses and legumes are perennials.

Structure of the Seed

Plants are also classified as *dicotyledons* and *monocotyledons* according to the structure of the seed.

DICOTYLEDONS

A good example of a dicotyledon seed is the broad bean because it is large and easy to study. If a pod of the broad bean plant is opened when it is nearly ripe it will be seen that each seed is attached to the inside of the pod by a short stalk called the *funicle*. All the nourishment which the developing seed requires passes through the funicle from the bean plant.

When the seed is ripe and has separated from the pod a black scar, known as the *hilum*, can be seen where the funicle was attached. Near one end of this hilum is a minute hole called the *micropyle* (see Fig. 5).

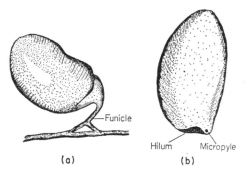

FIG. 5. (a) Bean seed attached to the inside of the pod by the funicle, (b) bean seed showing the hilum and micropyle.

If a bean is soaked in water the seed coat can be removed easily and all that is left is largely made up of the *embryo (germ)*. This consists of two seed leaves, or *cotyledons*, which contain the food for the young seedling.

Lying between the two cotyledons is the *radicle*, which eventually forms the *primary root*, and a continuation of the radicle the other end, the *plumule* (see Fig. 6). This develops into the young *shoot*, and is the first *bud* of the plant.

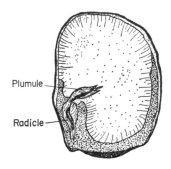

Plumule

Radicle

Fig. 6. Bean seed with one cotyledon removed.

MONOCOTYLEDONS

This class includes all the cereals and grasses and it is, therefore, very important.

The wheat grain is a typical example. It is not a true seed (it should be called a single-seeded fruit). The seed completely fills the whole grain, being practically united with the inside wall of the grain or fruit.

This fruit wall is made up of many different layers which are separated on milling into varying degrees of fineness, e.g. bran and pollards, and these are valuable livestock feed.

Most of the interior of the grain is taken up by the floury *endosperm*. The embryo occupies the small raised area at the base. The *scutellum*, a shield-like structure, separates the embryo from the endosperm. Attached to the base of the scutellum are the five roots of the embryo, one primary and two pairs of *secondary* rootlets. The roots are enclosed by a sheath called the *coleorhiza*. The position of the radicle and the plumule can be seen in the diagram (Fig. 7).

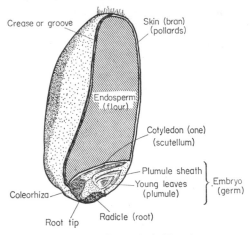

FIG. 7. Wheat grain cut in half at the crease.

The scutellum can be regarded as the cotyledon of the seed. There is only *one* cotyledon present and so wheat is a monocotyledon.

GERMINATION OF THE BEAN—THE DICOTYLEDON

Given suitable conditions for germination, i.e. water, heat and air, the seed coat of the dormant but living seed splits near the micropyle, and the radicle begins to grow downwards through this split to form the main, or primary root, from which lateral branches will soon develop (see Fig. 8)

When the root is firmly held in the soil, the plumule starts to grow by pushing its way out of the same opening in the seed coat. As it grows upwards its tip is bent to protect it from injury in passing through the soil, but it straightens out on reaching the surface, and *leaves* very quickly develop from the plumular shoot.

With the broad bean the cotyledons remain underground—
gradually giving up their stored food materials to the developing
plant, but with the French bean, and many other dicotyledon
seeds, the cotyledons are brought above ground with the plumule.

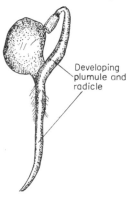

Developing
plumule and
radicle

FIG. 8. Germination of the bean, one cotyledon removed.

GERMINATION OF WHEAT—THE MONOCOTYLEDON

When the grain germinates the coleorhiza expands and splits
open the seed coat, and at the same time the roots break through
the coleorhiza (see Fig. 9).

The primary root is soon formed, supported by the two pairs of
secondary rootlets, but this root system (the seminal roots) is only
temporary and is soon replaced by *adventitious* roots (see Figs. 10
and 14). As the first root system is being formed at the base of the
stem so the plumule starts to grow upwards, and its first leaf, the
coleoptile, appears above the ground as a single pale tube-like
structure.

From a slit in the top of the leaf there appears the first *true leaf*
which is quickly followed by others, the younger leaves growing
from the older leaves (see Fig. 11).

As the wheat embryo grows so the floury endosperm is used up by
the developing roots and plumule, and the scutellum has the
important function of changing the endosperm into digestible food
for the growing parts.

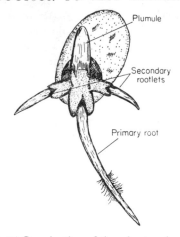

FIG. 9. Germination of the wheat grain.

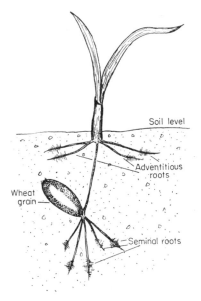

FIG. 10. Developing wheat plant.

With the broad bean, the cotyledons provide the food for the early nutrition of the plant, whilst the wheat grain is dependent upon the endosperm and scutellum, and in both cases it is not until the plumule has reached the light and turned green that the plants can begin to be independent.

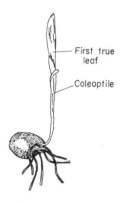

FIG. 11. Seedling wheat plant.

This point is important in relation to the depth at which seeds should be sown. Small seeds, such as the clovers and many of the grasses, must, as far as possible, be sown very shallow. Their food reserves will be exhausted before the shoot reaches the surface if sown too deeply. Larger seeds, such as the beans and peas, can and should be sown deeper.

When the leaves of the plant begin to manufacture food by photosynthesis (see p. 1) and when the primary root has established itself sufficiently well to absorb minerals from the soil (see p. 7) then the plant can develop independently, provided there is sufficient moisture and air present.

The main differences between the two groups of plants can be summarized as follows:

Dicotyledons	*Monocotyledons*
The embryo has two seed leaves.	The embryo has one seed leaf.
A primary root system is developed and persists.	A primary root system is developed, but is replaced by an adventitious root system.
Usually broad-leafed plants, e.g. clovers, cabbage and potato.	Usually narrow-leaved plants, e.g. the cereals and grasses, and most bulbous plants.

These two great groups of flowering plants can be further divided in the following way:

Families or orders e.g. The legume family, potato, the grasses and cereals.

Genus   Clovers of the legume family, and wheat of the cereal family.

Species   Red clover.

Variety   Broad red clover.

Strain   S151 broad red clover.

Plant Structure

The plant can be divided into two parts:

1. THE ROOT SYSTEM

The root system is concerned with the parts of the plant growing in the soil and there are two main types:

(a) *The tap root or primary root system*

This is made up of the primary root called the tap root with *lateral secondary* roots branching out from it, and from these *tertiary* roots may develop obliquely to form, in some cases, a very extensive system of roots (see Fig. 12).

The root of the bean plant is a good example of a tap root system, and if this is split it will be seen that there is a slightly darker central woody core; this is the *skeleton* if the root. It helps to anchor the plant, and also transports foodstuffs. The lateral secondary roots arise from this central core (see Fig. 13).

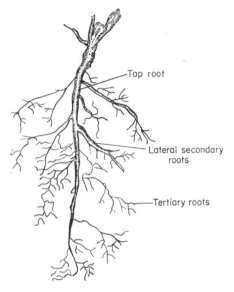

FIG. 12. Tap root or primary root system.

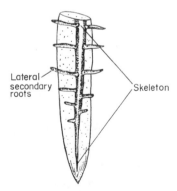

FIG. 13. Tap root of the bean plant.

Carrots, and other true root crops, such as sugar-beet and man-golds, have very well-developed tap roots. These biennials store food in their roots during the first year of growth to be used in the following year for the production of the flowering shoot and seeds. However, they are normally harvested after one season and the roots are used as food for man and stock.

(b) *The adventitious root system*

This is found on all grasses and cereals, and it is, in fact, the main root system of most monocotyledons. The primary root is quickly replaced by adventitious roots, which arise from the base of the stem (see Fig. 14).

Actually, these roots can develop from any part of the stem, and they are found on some dicotyledons as well, but not as the main root system, e.g. underground stems of the potato.

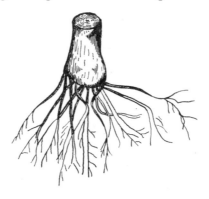

FIG. 14. Adventitious root system.

Root hairs (see Fig. 4)

These are very small white hair-like structures which are found near the tips of all roots. As the root grows, the hairs on the older parts die off, and others develop on the younger parts of the root.

Root hairs play a very important part in the life of the plant (see p. 5).

2. THE STEM

The second part of the flowering plant is the shoot which normally grows upright above the ground. It is made up of a main stem, branches, leaves and flowers.

Stems are either soft (*herbaceous*) or hard (*woody*) and in British agriculture it is only the soft and green herbaceous stems which are of any importance. These usually die back every year.

How stems grow

All stems start life as *buds* and the increase in length takes place at the tip of the shoot called the *terminal* bud.

If a Brussels sprout is cut lengthwise and examined, it will be seen that the young leaves arise from the bud *axis*. This axis is made up of different types of cell tissue, which is continually making new cells and thus growing (see Fig. 15).

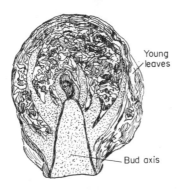

Young leaves

Bud axis

FIG. 15. Longitudinal section of a Brussels sprout.

Stems are usually jointed, each joint forming a *node*, and the part between two nodes is the *internode*. At the nodes the stem is usually solid and thicker, and this swelling is caused by the storing up of material at the base of the leaf (see Fig. 16).

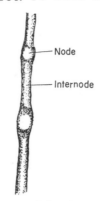

FIG. 16. Jointed stem.

The bud consists of closely packed leaves arising from a number of nodes. It is, in fact, a condensed portion of the stem which develops by a lengthening of the internodes.

Axillary buds are formed in the angle between the stem and the leaf stalk. These buds, which are similar to the terminal bud, develop to form lateral *branches, leaves* and *flowers*.

Some modification of stems

(1) A *stolon* is a stem which grows along the ground surface. Adventitious roots are produced at the nodes, and buds on the runner can develop into upright shoots, and separate plants can be formed, e.g. strawberry plants (see Fig. 17).

(2) A *rhizome* is similar to a stolon but grows under the surface of the ground, e.g. couch grass (see Fig. 17).

(3) A *tuber* is really a modified rhizome. The end of the rhizomes swell to form tubers. The tuber is therefore a swollen stem. The potato is a well-known example, and it has "eyes" which are really buds and these develop shoots when the potato tuber is planted.

(4) A *tendril* is found on certain legumes, such as the pea. The terminal leaflet is modified as in the diagram. This is useful for climbing purposes to support the plant (see Fig. 18).

Corms and *suckers* are other examples of modified stems.

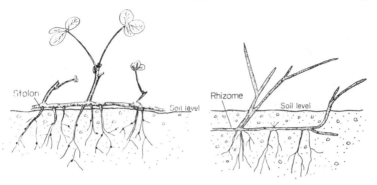

Fig. 17. Modified stems.

Fig. 18. Modified stem.

THE LEAF

Leaves in all cases arise from buds. They are extremely important organs, being not only responsible for the manufacture of sugar and starch from the atmosphere for the growing parts of the plant, but they also are the organs through which transpiration of water takes place.

B

A typical leaf of a dicotyledon consists of three main parts:

(1) The *blade*.
(2) The *stalk* or *petiole*.
(3) The *basal sheath* connecting the leaf to the stem. This may be modified as with legumes into a pair of wing-like *stipules* (see Figs. 19(a), 49–51).

The blade is the most obvious part of the leaf and it is made up of a network of veins.

There are two main types of dicotyledonous leaves:

(1) A prominent central *midrib*, from which lateral veins branch off on either side. These side veins branch into smaller and smaller ones, as in the diagram (see Fig. 19).
(2) No single midrib, but several main ribs spread out from the top of the leaf stalk; between these the finer veins spread out as before, e.g. horse-chestnut leaf (see Fig. 19).

The veins are the essential supply lines for the process of photosynthesis. They consist of two main parts, one for bringing the required raw material up to the leaf (*xylem*), and the other part being concerned with carrying the finished product away from the leaf (*phloem*).

Leaves can show great variation in shape and type of margin, as in Fig. 19. They can also be divided into two broad classes as follows:

(1) *Simple* leaves. The blade consists of one continuous piece (see Fig. 19(a)).
(2) *Compound* leaves. Simple leaves may become deeply lobed and when the division between the lobes reaches the midrib it is a compound leaf, and the separate parts of the blade are called the *leaflets* (see Fig. 19(b)).

The blade surface may be *smooth* (glabrous) or *hairy*, according to variety, and this is important in legumes because it can affect its palatability to stock.

Monocotyledonous leaves are dealt with in the section on "Grassland".

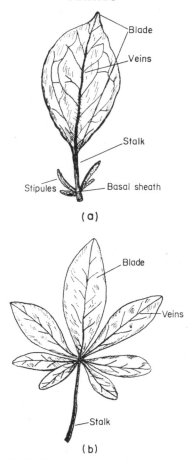

Fig. 19. (a) Simple leaf, (b) Compound leaf.

Modified leaves

(a) *Cotyledons* or seed leaves are usually of a very simple form.

(b) *Scales* are normally rather thin, yellowish to brown membranous leaf structures, very variable in size and form. On woody stems they are present as *bud scales* which protect the bud, and they are also found on rhizomes such as couch.

(c) *Leaf tendrils.* The terminal leaflet like the stem can be modified into thin threadlike structures, e.g. pea and vetch.

Other examples of modified leaves are *leaf-spines* and *bracts*.

THE FLOWER

In the centre of the flower is the *axis* which is simply the continuation of the flower stalk. It is known as the *receptacle*, and on it are arranged four kinds of organs:

(1) The lowermost is a ring of green leaves called the *calyx*, made up of individual *sepals*.

(2) Immediately above the calyx is a ring of *petals* known as the *corolla*.

(3) Above the corolla are the *stamens*, again arranged in a ring. They are similar in appearance to an ordinary match, the swollen tip being called the *anther* which, when ripe, contains the *pollen grains*.

(4) The highest position on the receptacle is occupied by the *pistil* which is made up of one or a series of small green bottle-shaped bodies—the *carpel*, which is itself made up of three parts: the *stigma*, *style*, and the *ovary* (containing *ovules*). It is within the ovary that the future *seeds* are produced (see Figs. 20 and 21).

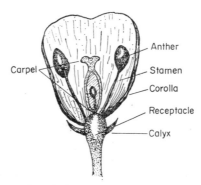

FIG. 20. Longitudinal section of a simple flower.

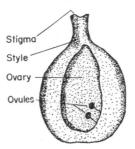

FIG. 21. Carpel.

Most flowers are more complicated in appearance than the above, but basically they consist of these four main parts.

THE FORMATION OF SEEDS

Pollination precedes *fertilization*, which is the union of the male and female reproductive cells. When pollination takes place the pollen grain is transferred from the anther to the stigma. This may be *self-pollination* where the pollen is transferred from the anther to the stigma of the same flower, or *cross-pollination* when it is carried to a different flower (see Fig. 22).

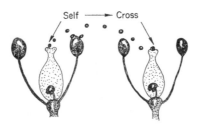

FIG. 22. Self- and cross-pollination.

With fertilization the pollen grain grows down the style of the carpel to fuse with the ovule. After fertilization, changes take place whereby the ovule develops into the embryo, and endosperm may be formed according to the species. This makes up the *seed*. The ovary also changes after fertilization to form the *fruit*, as distinct from the seed.

With the grasses and cereals there is only one seed formed in the fruit and, being so closely united with the inside wall of the ovary, it cannot easily be separated from it.

The one-seeded fruit is called a *grain*.

THE INFLORESCENCE

Special branches of the plant are modified to bear the flowers, and they form the inflorescence. There are two main types of inflorescence:

(1) Where the branches bearing the flowers continue to grow, so that the youngest flowers are nearest the apex and the oldest farthest away—*indefinite* inflorescence (see Fig. 23(a)).

A well known example of this inflorescence is the *spike* found in many species of grasses.

(a)

FIG. 23. (a) Indefinite inflorescence.

(2) Where the main stem is terminated by a single flower and ceases to grow in length; any further growth takes place by lateral branches, and they eventually terminate in a single flower and growth is stopped—*definite* inflorescence, e.g. stitchworts (see Fig. 23(b)).

There are many variations of these two main types of inflorescence.

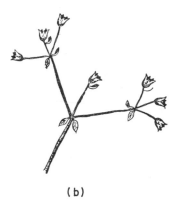

(b)

FIG. 23. (b) Definite inflorescence.

What Plants Need

To grow satisfactorily a plant needs *warmth, light, water, carbon dioxide* and about a dozen other *chemical elements* which it can obtain from the soil.

WARMTH

Most crop plants in this country start growing when the average daily temperature is above 42°F (6°C). Growth is best between 60°F (16°C) and 80°F (27°C). These temperatures apply to thermometer readings taken in the shade about 4 ft above ground. Crops grown in hotter countries usually have higher temperature requirements.

Cold frosty conditions may seriously damage plant growth. Crop plants differ in their ability to withstand very cold conditions. For example, winter rye and wheat can stand colder conditions than winter oats. Potato plants and stored tubers are easily damaged by frost. Sugar-beet may bolt (go to seed) if there are frosts after germination; frost in December and January may destroy crops left in the ground.

LIGHT

Without light, plants cannot produce carbohydrates and will soon die. The amount of photosynthesis which takes place daily in a plant is partly due to the length of daylight and partly to the intensity of the sunlight. Bright sunlight is of most importance where there is dense plant growth.

The lengths of daylight and darkness periods vary according to the distance from the equator and also from season to season. This can affect the flowering and seeding of crop plants and is one of the limiting factors in introducing new crops into a country. Grasses are now being tested in this country which will remain leafy and not produce flowering shoots under the daylight conditions here.

WATER

Water is an essential part of all plant cells and it is also required in extravagant amounts for the process of transpiration. Water carries nutrients from the soil into and through the plant and also carries the products of photosynthesis from the leaves to wherever they are needed. Plants take up about 200 tons of water for every ton of dry matter produced.

CARBON DIOXIDE (CO_2)

Plants need carbon dioxide for photosynthesis. This is taken into the leaves through the stomata and so the amount which can go in is affected by the rate of transpiration. Another limiting factor is the small amount (0.03%) of carbon dioxide in the atmosphere.

The percentage can increase just above the surface of soils rich in organic matter where soil bacteria are active and releasing carbon dioxide. This is possibly one of the reasons why crops grow better on such soils.

CHEMICAL ELEMENTS REQUIRED BY PLANTS

In order that a plant may build up its cell structure and function as a food factory many simple chemical substances are needed. These are taken into the roots from the soil solution and the clay particles. Those required in fairly large amounts (a few pounds to one or more hundredweight per acre) are called the *major* nutrients; those required in small amounts (part of an ounce to several pounds per acre) are the *minor* nutrients or *trace elements*.

The major nutrients	Use	Source
Carbon (C) Hydrogen (H) Oxygen (O)	Used in making carbohydrates.	The air and water.
Nitrogen (N)	Very important for building proteins.	Organic matter (including F.Y.M.). Nodules on leguminous plants. Nitrogen fertilizers such as ammonium and nitrate compounds and urea. Nitrogen-fixing soil micro-organisms.
Phosphorus (P) (phosphate)	Essential for cell division and many chemical reactions.	Small amounts from the mineral and organic matter in the soil. Mainly from phosphatic fertilizers, e.g. superphosphate, ground rock phosphate, basic slag and compounds, and residues of previous fertilizer applications.
Potassium (K) (potash)	Helps with formation of carbohydrates and proteins. Regulates water in and through the plant.	Small amounts from mineral and organic matter in the soil. Potash fertilizers, e.g. muriate and sulphate of potash.

The major nutrients	Use	Source
Calcium (Ca)	Essential for development of growth tissue, e.g. root tips.	Usually enough in the soil. Applied as chalk or limestone to neutralize acidity.
Magnesium (Mg)	A necessary part of chlorophyll.	If soil is deficient, may be added as magnesium limestone or magnesium sulphate.
Sulphur (S)	Part of many proteins and some oils.	Usually enough in the soil. Added in some fertilizers (e.g. sulphate of ammonia) and gypsum.

The trace elements are:

	Deficiency symptoms	Remedy
Boron (B)	*Heart-rot* in sugar-beet and mangolds. *Brown-heart* (*raan*) in turnips and swedes.	20 lb borax per acre evenly spread, e.g. with fertilizer.
Manganese (Mn)	*Grey leaf or speck* in cereals. "*Marsh-spot*" in peas. *Speckled yellowing* of leaves of sugar-beet.	Manganese sulphate applied to soil ($\frac{1}{2}$–1 cwt/acre) or 10 lb sprayed on young crop, or 14 lb combine drilled (cereals).

Deficiencies of boron and manganese are often caused by using too much lime.

Other trace elements are chlorine, copper, iron, molybdenum and zinc, but these rarely cause trouble on most farm soils.

Cobalt is not considered necessary for plant growth, but animals feeding on plants deficient in cobalt (e.g. on some all-grass areas) waste away ("pine").

The remedy would be a few pounds of a cobalt salt per acre or in a salt lick.

Sodium does not appear to be essential, but some crops such as sugar-beet and mangolds grow better if it is applied (e.g. as common salt). It may partly replace potassium.

The effects of nitrogen, phosphorus and potassium are discussed more fully in the chapter on "Fertilizers".

Legumes and the Nitrogen Cycle

Legumes are plants which have several interesting characteristics such as:

(1) A special type of fruit called a legume, which splits along both sides to release its seeds, e.g. pea pod.

(2) The flowers closely resemble pea flowers.

(3) Nodules (lumps) on their roots contain special types of bacteria which can "fix" (convert) nitrogen from the air into nitrogen compounds. These bacteria enter the plant through the root hairs from the surrounding soil.

This "fixation" of nitrogen is of considerable agricultural importance. Many of our farm crops are legumes, for example, *peas, beans, vetches, lupins, clovers, lucerne (alfalfa), sainfoin* and *trefoil*. The bacteria obtain carbodydrates (energy) from the plant and in return they supply nitrogen compounds. The nodules can release nitrogen compounds into the soil. These compounds are changed to nitrates and taken up by neighbouring plants (e.g. by grasses in a grass and clover sward) or by the following crop, e.g. wheat after clover or beans. The amount of nitrogen which can be "fixed" by legume bacteria varies widely; estimates of 50–400 lb of nitrogen per acre have been made. Some of the reasons for variations are:

(a) *The type of plant.* Some crop plants "fix" more nitrogen than others, e.g. lucerne and clovers (especially if grazed) are usually better than peas and beans.

(b) *The conditions in the soil.* The bacteria usually work best in soils which favour the growth of the plant on which they live.

A good supply of calcium and phosphate in the soil is usually beneficial, although lupins grow well on acid soils.

(c) *The strains of bacteria present.* Most soils in this country contain the strains of bacteria required for most of the leguminous crops which are grown. Lucerne (alfalfa) is an exception and it is common practice to coat the lucerne seed with the proper bacterial culture before sowing; these bacteria will later enter the roots of the young plant.

The Nitrogen Cycle

The circulation of nitrogen (in various compounds such as, nitrates and proteins) as found on the farm is illustrated diagrammatically in Fig. 24.

Atmospheric nitrogen is "fixed" (combined) in compounds by *legume nodule bacteria,* by various *nitrogen-fixing micro-organisms,* by *thunderstorms* and in the manufacture of *nitrogen fertilizers.*

Simple nitrogen compounds (mainly nitrates) are taken up by plants to form plant proteins which may then be eaten by animals to form animal proteins. Dead plants and animals, and the faeces and urine of animals are broken down by decay micro-organisms to leave simple nitrogen compounds in the soil.

The denitrifying bacteria change nitrogen compounds back to free nitrogen. This is most likely to happen where nitrates are abundant and oxygen is in short-supply, e.g. in waterlogged soils.

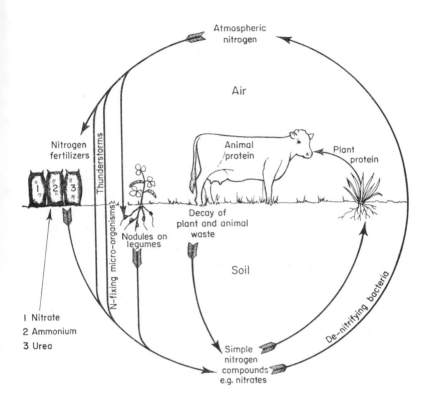

FIG. 24. The nitrogen cycle.

Suggestions for Classwork

1. Compare and contrast the dicotyledon seed and the monocotyledon seed.
2. Germinate the bean seed, and study its development.
3. Dig up and carefully examine the root system of different plants.
4. Examine different types of modified stems.
5. Examine different leaves and modified leaves.
6. With a magnifying glass, examine carefully the parts of a flower.

CHAPTER 2

SOILS

SOILS are very complex natural formations which make up the surface of the earth. They provide a suitable environment in which plants may obtain *water, nutrients, oxygen* for root respiration, and firm *anchorage*. Soils are formed by the weathering of rocks, followed by the growth and decay of plants, animals, and soil micro-organisms. If a farmer is to provide the best possible conditions for crop growth, it is desirable that he should understand what soils are, how they were formed and how they should be managed.

The *topsoil* or *surface soil* is a layer about 3–18 in. deep which may be taken as the greatest depth which a farmer would plough or cultivate and in which most of the plant roots are found. Loose, cultivated, top soil is sometimes called *mould*.

The *subsoil*, which lies underneath, is an intermediate stage in the formation of soil from the rock below.

A *soil profile* is a section taken through the soil down to the parent rock. In some cases this may consist of only a shallow surface soil (4–6 in.) on top of a rock such as chalk or limestone. In other well developed soils (several feet deep) there are usually three or more definite layers (or horizons) which vary in colour, texture and compaction (see Fig. 25).

The soil profile can be examined by digging a trench or by taking out cores of soil from various depths with a *soil auger*.

A careful examination of the layers (horizons) can be useful in forming an opinion as to how the soil was formed, its natural drainage and how it might be farmed. Some detailed soil classifications are based on soil profile.

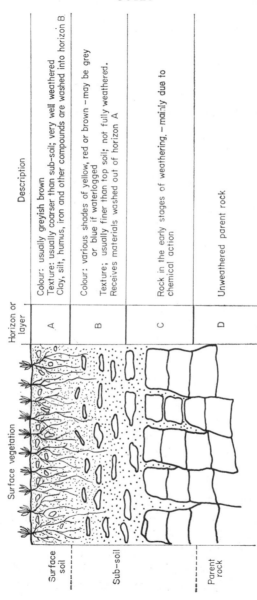

Horizon or layer	Description
A	Colour: usually greyish brown Texture: usually coarser than sub-soil; very well weathered Clay, silt, humus, iron and other compounds are washed into horizon B
B	Colour: various shades of yellow, red or brown – may be grey or blue if waterlogged Texture; usually finer than top soil; not fully weathered. Receives materials washed out of horizon A
C	Rock in the early stages of weathering, – mainly due to chemical action
D	Unweathered parent rock

Surface vegetation

Surface soil

Sub-soil

Parent rock

FIG. 25. Soil profile diagram showing the breakdown of rock to form various soil layers (horizons).

Soil Formation

There are very many different types of soils and subsoils. The differences are mainly due to the variety of rocks from which they are formed. However, other factors such as *climate*, *topography*, *plant and animal life*, the *age of the developing soil material* and *farming operations* also affect the type of soil which develops.

THE MORE IMPORTANT ROCK FORMATIONS

Igneous or primary rocks, e.g. *granite* (coarse crystals) and *basalt* (fine crystals). These rocks were formed from the very hot molten material which made up the earth, millions of years ago. The minerals (chemical compounds) in these rocks are mostly in the form of crystals and are the primary source of the minerals found in all our soils. Igneous rocks are very hard and weather very slowly. Clay and sand are break down products.

Sedimentary or transported rocks. These have been formed from weathered material (e.g. clay, silt and sand) carried and deposited by water and wind. The sediments later became compressed by more material on top and cemented to form new rocks such as *sandstones*, *clays* and *shales*.

The *chalks* and *limestones* were formed from the shells and skeletons of sea animals of various sizes. These rocks are mainly calcium carbonate but in some cases are magnesium carbonate. The calcareous soils are formed from them (see p. 56).

Metamorphic rocks, e.g. *marble* (from limestone) and *slate* (from shale). These are rocks which have been changed in various ways.

ORGANIC MATTER

Deep deposits of *organic matter* (humus) are found in places where waterlogged soil conditions did not allow the breakdown of dead plant material by micro-organisms and oxidation.

Peats have been formed in water-logged acidic areas where the vegetation is mainly mosses, rushes, heather and some trees.

Black fen (muck soil) has been formed in marshy river estuary conditions where the water was hard (lime rich) and often silty; the plants were mainly reeds, sedges, rushes and some trees.

Good drainage is necessary before preparing these areas for cropping.

GLACIAL DRIFT

Many soils in the British Isles are not derived from the rocks underneath but are deposits carried from other rock formations by glaciers, e.g. boulder clays. This makes the study of our soils very complicated.

Alluvium is material which has been deposited recently, for example, by river flooding. This material is very variable in composition.

WEATHERING OF ROCKS

The breakdown of rocks is mainly caused by the *physical* and *chemical* effects of the weather.

Physical weathering

Changes of temperature cause the various mineral crystals in rocks to expand and contract by different amounts, and so cracking and shattering often occurs.

Water, freezing in cracks in the rock, expands and causes more shattering. The pieces of rock broken off in this way are usually sharp-edged, but if they are carried and knocked about by glaciers, rivers or wind, they become more rounded in shape, e.g. sand and stones in a river bed.

Wetting and drying of some rocks such as clays and shales causes expansion and contraction and results in cracking and flaking.

Chemical weathering

Chemical breakdown of the mineral matter in a developing soil is brought about by the action of water, oxygen, carbon dioxide and nitric acid from the atmosphere; and by carbonic and organic acids from the biological activity in the soil. The soil water, which is a weak acid, dissolves some minerals and allows chemical reactions to take place.

Water can also unite with substances in the soil (hydration) to form new substances which are more bulky and so can cause shattering of rock fragments.

Clay is produced by chemical weathering. In the case of rocks such as granite, when the clay producing parts are weathered away the more resistant quartz crystals are left as sand or silt.

In the later stages of chemical weathering the soil minerals are broken down to release plant nutrients—this is a continuing process in most soils.

Other Factors in Soil Formation

CLIMATE

The rate of weathering partly depends on the climate. For example, the wide variations in temperature and the high rainfall of the tropics makes for much faster soil development than would be possible in the colder and drier climatic regions.

TOPOGRAPHY

The depth of soil can be considerably affected by the slope of the ground. Weathered soil tends to erode from steep slopes and build up on the flatter land at the bottom. Level land is more likely to produce uniform weathering.

BIOLOGICAL ACTIVITY

Plants, animals and micro-organisms, during their life-cycles, leave many organic substances in the soil. Some of the substances may dissolve some of the mineral material; dead material may partially decompose to give *humus*.

The roots of plants may open up cracks in the soil.

Vegetation such as mosses and lichens can attack and break down the surface of rocks.

Holes made in the soil by burrowing animals such as earthworms, moles, rabbits, etc., help to breakdown soft and partly weathered rocks.

FARMING OPERATIONS

Deep ploughing and cultivation, artificial drainage, liming, etc., can speed up the soil formation processes very considerably.

The Physical Make-up of Soil and its Effect on Plant Growth

The farmer must consider the soil from the point of view of its ability to grow crops. To produce good crops the soil must provide suitable conditions in which plant roots can grow. It must also supply nutrients, water and air; and the temperature must be suitable for the growth of the crop.

The soil is composed of:

Solids	Mainly *mineral matter* (stones, sand, silt, clay, etc.) and *organic matter*—remains of plants and animals.
Liquids	Mainly *soil water* (a weak acid).
Gases	*Soil air* (competes with water to occupy the spaces between the particles).
Living organisms	Micro-organisms such as bacteria, fungi, small soil animals, earthworms, etc.

MINERAL MATTER

This weathered material, and especially the clay part, is mainly responsible for making a soil difficult or easy to work. It may provide many plant nutrients—but *not* nitrogen. The farmer normally cannot alter the mineral matter in a soil (but see "*Claying*").

The amounts of clay, silt and sand which a soil contains can be measured by a *mechanical analysis* of a sample in the laboratory (see Table 1, Types of Soil).

ORGANIC MATTER

Unlike mineral matter, the amount of organic matter in a soil can vary very considerably from time to time. In most fertile soils it is about 3–5% of the dry weight of the soil, but organic soils (e.g. black Fens and peats) consist almost entirely of organic matter. It may remain for a short time in the undecayed state and as such can help to "open-up" the soil—this could be harmful on sandy soils. However, the organic matter is soon attacked by all sorts of soil organisms—bacteria, fungi, earthworms, insects, etc. When they have finished eating and digesting it and each other a complex, dark coloured, structureless material called *humus* remains.

The amount of humus formed is greatest from plants which have a lot of strengthening (lignified) tissue (e.g. straw). Humus is finally broken down by an oxidation process which is not fully understood.

The amount of humus which can remain in a soil is fairly constant for any particular type of soil. The addition of more organic matter often does not alter the humus content appreciably because the rate of breakdown increases. Organic matter is broken down most rapidly in warm, moist soils which are well limed and well aerated. Break down is slowest in waterlogged, acid conditions.

The chemical make-up of humus is not fully understood but its effects on the soil are well known.

Like clay, it is a *colloid* (i.e. it is a gluey substance which behaves like a sponge—it absorbs water and swells up when wetted and shrinks on drying). The humus colloids are not so gummy and plastic as the clay colloids but they can improve light (sandy) soils by binding groups of particles together. This reduces the size of the pores (spaces between the particles) and increases the water-holding capacity. Humus can also improve clay soils by making them less plastic and by assisting in the formation of a crumb structure— lime must also be present. Earthworms help in this soil improvement by digesting the clay and humus material with lime.

Plant nutrients—particularly nitrogen and phosphorous—are released for uptake by other plants when organic matter breaks down. The humus colloids can hold bases such as potassium and ammonia in an available form. In these ways it has a very beneficial effect in promoting steady crop growth.

Organic matter in the soil may be maintained or increased by growing *leys*, working-in *straw* and similar *crop residues*, *farmyard manure*, *composts*, etc. The roots and stubble are usually sufficient to maintain an adequate humus content in a soil growing cereals continuously.

In areas where erosion by wind and water is common, mineral soils are less likely to suffer damage if they are well supplied with humus.

Where it is possible to grow good leys and utilize them fully, this is one of the best ways of maintaining a high level of organic matter and a good soil structure.

Increasing the organic matter (humus) content of a soil is the best way of increasing its water holding capacity: 20–25 ton/acre of well rotted F.Y.M. may increase the amount of water which can be held by 25% or more.

Water in the Soil

Soils vary in their capacity to hold water and, to understand why this is, it is necessary to understand some of the differences between soils.

The soil is a mass of irregular-shaped particles forming a network of spaces or channels called the *pore space*, which may be filled with air or water or both. If the pore space is completely filled with water the soil is *waterlogged* and unsuitable for plant growth because the roots need oxygen for respiration. Ideally, there should be about equal volumes of air and water.

When the soil particles are small (e.g. clay) then the spaces between the particles are also small; and when they are large (e.g. sand) the spaces are large. However, although the spaces are small in a clay soil there are very many more spaces than in the same volume of a sandy soil. In a clay soil about half of the total volume is pore space whereas in a sandy soil only about one third is pore space. These volumes refer to dry soils. The pore space may be altered by a change in:

(a) grouping of the soil particles (i.e. structure),
(b) amount of organic matter (humus) present,
(c) compaction of the soil.

The fact that clay soils have a greater pore space than sandy soils partly explains why the clay soil can hold more water.

Another important factor is the *surface area* of the particles.

Water is held as a thin layer or film around the soil particles. The smaller the particles the stronger are the attractive forces holding the water. Also, the smaller the particles the greater is the surface area per unit volume. (Compare boxes filled with billiard balls, marbles and small ball-bearings.) A comparison for pure materials is set out below.

Material	Particle size (mm)	Surface area
Coarse sand	2·0	×
Finest sand	0·02	100 ×
Finest silt	0·002	1,000 ×
Finest clay		100,000 ×

The surface area of the particles in a cubic foot of fine clay may be over 100 acres.

The organic matter (humus) in the soil also holds water.

The water in the soil comes from rainfall, or, in dry areas, from irrigation.

When water falls on a dry soil it does *not* become evenly distributed through the soil. The topmost layer becomes saturated first and as more water is added the depth of the saturated layer increases. In this layer most of the pore space is filled with water. However, a well-drained soil cannot hold all of this water for very long. After a day or so some of the water will soak into the lower layers or run away in drains. The amount of water which is then retained by the soil is called the *moisture-holding capacity* or *field capacity*. The amount of water which can be held in this way varies according to the texture, and structure of the soil (see pp. 46 and 73). The weight of water held by a clay soil may be equal to the weight of the soil particles, whereas a sandy soil may hold less than one-tenth of the weight of the particles. The water-holding capacity of a soil is usually expressed in inches, e.g. a clay soil may have a field capacity of 5 in./ft. in depth.

The ways in which water is retained in the soil can be summarized as follows:

(a) as a film around the soil particles,
(b) in the organic matter,
(c) filling some of the smaller spaces,
(d) chemically combined with the soil minerals.

Most of this water can be easily taken up by plant roots but as the soil dries out the remaining water is more firmly held and eventually a stage is reached when no more water can be extracted by the plant. This is called the *wilting point* because plants wilt permanently and soon die. This *permanent wilting* should not be confused with the *temporary wilting* which sometimes occurs on very hot days because the rate of transpiration is greater than the rate of water absorption through the roots; in these cases the plants recover during the night or earlier. The water which can be taken up by the plant roots is called the *available water*. It is the difference between the amounts at field capacity and wilting point. In clay soils only about 50–60% of "field capacity" water is available; in sandy soils up to 90% or more may be available. Although plants may not die until the wilting point is reached, they will suffer from shortage of water as it becomes more difficult to extract (see Fig. 26).

Water in the soil tends to hold the particles together and lumps of soil may stick together. When a loam or heavy soil is at or above half field capacity it is possible to form it into a ball which will not fall apart when handled and tossed about. At wilting point, the soil is crumbly and will not hold together. So, if irrigation is economically possible, it should be used before the soil dries out to a state in which it will not hold together.

Some of the water in soils with very small pores and channels can move through the soil by *capillary forces*, i.e. surface tension between the water and the walls of the fine tubes or capillaries. This is a very slow movement and may not be fast enough to supply plant roots in a soil which is drying out. Heavy rolling of a soil may reduce the size of the pores and so set up some capillary action.

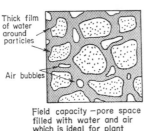

Thick film of water around particles

Air bubbles

Field capacity —pore space filled with water and air which is ideal for plant growth

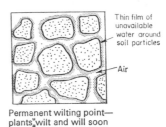

Thin film of unavailable water around soil particles

Air

Permanent wilting point— plants wilt and will soon die due to lack of water

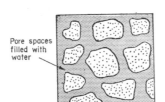

Pore spaces filled with water

Waterlogged or saturated—no air present and so crop plants die or grow very slowly

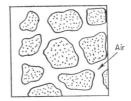

Air

Dry—no water present and so plants die— this is unlikely to happen in a field

Fig. 26. Highly magnified particles and pores showing how water and air may be found in the soil.

Water is lost from the soil by *evaporation* from the surface and by *transpiration* through plants. It moves very slowly from the body of the soil to the surface, so after the top 1 or 2 in. have dried out the loss of water by evaporation is very small. Cultivations increase evaporation losses. Most of the water is taken up by plants (during the growing season) and, in open-textured soils, air moves in to fill the pore space. In the case of clay, however, air cannot move in fast enough through the very small pore channels and so this type of soil shrinks and cracks—vertically and horizontally—and then air can get in through the cracks which are formed.

The water which enters the soil soon becomes a dilute solution of the soluble soil chemicals. It dissolves some of the carbon dioxide in the soil and so becomes a weak acid.

SOIL AERATION

Plant roots and many of the soil animals and micro-organisms require oxygen for respiration and give out carbon dioxide. The air found in the soil is really atmospheric air which has been changed by these activities, (and also by various chemical reactions), and so contains less oxygen and much more carbon dioxide. After a time this reduction in oxygen and increase in carbon dioxide becomes harmful to the plant and other organisms.

Aeration is the replacement of this stagnant soil air with fresh air. The process is mainly brought about by the movement of water into and out of the soil, e.g. rain water soaks into the soil filling many of the pore spaces and driving out the air. Then, as the surplus water soaks down to the drains or is taken up by plants, fresh air is drawn into the soil to refill the pore spaces.

Also, oxygen moves into the soil and carbon dioxide moves out of the soil by a diffusion process similar to what happens through the stomata in plant leaves.

The aeration process is also assisted by:

(1) changes in temperature,
(2) changes in barometric pressure,
(3) good drainage,
(4) cultivations—especially on clay soils and where a soil cap has formed,
(5) open soil structure.

Sandy soils are usually well aerated because of their open structure. Clay soils are usually poorly aerated—especially when the very small pores in such soils become filled with water. Good aeration is especially important for germinating seeds and seedling plants.

SOIL MICRO-ORGANISMS

There are thousands of millions of very small organisms in every ounce of fertile soil. Many different types are found but the main groups are:

(1) *Bacteria*—the most numerous group. Bacteria are the smallest type of single-celled organisms and can only be seen with a microscope. There are many kinds in the soil. Most of them feed on and breakdown organic matter. They obtain energy from the carbohydrates (e.g. sugar, starches, cellulose, etc.) and release carbon dioxide in the process. They also need nitrogen to build cell proteins. If they cannot get this protein from the organic matter they may use other sources such as the nitrogen applied as fertilizers. When this happens (e.g. where straw is ploughed in) the following crop may suffer from shortage of nitrogen unless extra fertilizer is applied. Some types of bacteria can convert (fix) the nitrogen from the air into nitrogen compounds which can be used by plants (see Legumes and the Nitrogen Cycle p. 29). Soil bacteria are most active in warm, damp, well aerated soils which are not acid.

(2) *Fungi*. Fungi are simple types of plants which feed on and break down organic matter. They are mainly responsible for breaking down lignified (woody) tissue. They have *no* chlorophyll or proper flowers. The fungi usually found in arable soils are very small, but larger types are found in other soils, e.g. peats. Fungi can live in acid conditions and in drier conditions than bacteria. (Mushrooms are fungi, and "fairy rings" are produced by fungi.) Sometimes disease-producing fungi develop in some fields, e.g. those causing "take-all" and "eyespot" in cereals.

(3) *Actinomycetes*. These are organisms which are intermediate between bacteria and fungi and have a similar effect on the soil. They need oxygen for growth and are more common in the drier, warmer soils. They are not so numerous as bacteria and fungi. Some types can cause plant diseases, e.g. common scab in potatoes (worst in light, dry soils).

(4) *Algae.* Soil algae are very small simple organisms which contain chlorophyll and so can build up their bodies by using carbon dioxide from the air and nitrogen from the soil. Algae grow well in fertile damp soils exposed to the sun. Algae growing in swampy (waterlogged) soils can use dissolved carbon dioxide from the water and release oxygen. This process is an important source of oxygen for crop plants such as rice. Algae are important in colonizing bare soils in the early stages of weathering.

(5) *Protozoa.* These are very small, single-celled animals. Most of them feed on bacteria and similar small organisms. A few types contain chlorophyll and so can produce carbohydrates like plants.

The activities of the micro-organisms in the soil are rather complex and as yet not fully understood, but we do know that they improve the productivity of the soil. In general, the more fertile the soil the more organisms there are present.

EARTHWORMS

It is generally believed that earthworms have a beneficial effect on the fertility of soils, particularly those under grass, but there is very little definite proof that they do any good on arable land. There are several different kinds found in our soils but most of their activities are very similar. They live in holes in the soil and feed on organic matter—either living plants or, more often, dead and decaying matter. They carry down into the soil fallen leaves and twigs, straw, and similar materials. Earthworms do not thrive in acid soils because they want plenty of calcium (lime) to digest with the organic matter they eat. Their casts, which are usually left on the surface, consist of a useful mixture of organic matter, mineral matter and lime. This material may weigh 10 ton or more per acre. The greatest numbers are found in loam soils (under grass) where there is usually a good supply of air, moisture, organic matter and lime. Various methods have been tried to estimate the numbers present in a soil but with limited success.

The many holes they make allow water to enter and drain from the soil very easily and this in turn draws fresh air in as it soaks downwards. This may not always be a good thing, because the holes often have a smooth and, in places, impervious lining which may allow the water to go through to the drains too easily instead of soaking into the soil.

Earthworms are the main food of the mole which does so much damage by burrowing and throwing up heaps of soil.

OTHER SOIL ANIMALS

In addition to earthworms there are many species of small animals present in most soils. They feed on living and decaying plant material and micro-organisms. Some of the common ones are: slugs, snails, millipedes, centipedes, ants, spiders, eelworms, beetles, larvae of various insects such as cutworms, leather jackets and wireworms. The farmer is only directly concerned with those which damage his crops or livestock. The more troublesome crop pests are dealt with in chapter 7.

Soil Texture and Structure

Soil texture is that characteristic which is determined by the amounts of clay, silt, sand and organic matter which the soil contains. This property normally cannot be altered by the farmer (but see "Claying"). Soil texture can be measured by a *mechanical analysis* of a sample in the laboratory and classified accordingly. (See Table 1, "Types of soil".)

Soil structure is the arrangement of the soil particles individually (e.g. grains of sand), in groups (e.g. crumbs or clods) or as a mixture of the two. It can be altered by: *weather conditions* (e.g. lumps changed to crumbs by frost action or alternate wetting and drying), *penetration of plant roots, cultivations,* etc. It is not possible to measure soil structure satisfactorily.

"Field texture" is the combined effect of texture and structure at any one time and can be assessed by the "feel" of a moist handful of the soil when rubbed between the fingers.

Clay is sticky, can be moulded, and will take a polish.

Silt feels silky, smooth and slightly sticky.

Sand feels gritty.

Organic matter usually feels soft and slightly sticky.

It is possible to classify the soil according to which "feeling" is dominant; if none is dominant then the soil is a loam. A skilled person may classify up to ten textures by this practical method.

The names commonly used to classify soils in this way are heavy or light, clayey, loamy or sandy. The terms "heavy" and "light" refer to the amount of power required to draw a plough or cultivator through the soil. A heavy (clayey) soil consists mainly of very small particles which pack tightly together whereas a light (sandy) soil consists mainly of large particles which are loosely held together because of the relatively large pore spaces.

Crumb structure is formed by the grouping together (aggregation) of the particles of clay, sand and silt. This aggregation is possible because there are positive and negative electric charges (forces) acting through the surface of the particles. These forces are strongest in clay and very weak in sand. This strong adhesive property of clay particles makes clay soils more difficult to work than sandy soils but it also enables them to form crumbs easily.

Water has special electric properties and its presence is necessary for the grouping (crumbing) of soil particles. The electric forces in the water and in the soil particles make the water stick as a thin film around the particles of soil. As this film becomes thinner (e.g. when soil is drying out) the particles are drawn closer together to form groups (crumbs). The particles in the crumbs may come apart again if the soil becomes very wet.

There must be lime present in the water if clay particles are to stick together to form porous crumbs. This partly explains why liming benefits clay soils.

If organic matter or an iron compound (ferric hydroxide) is present then the particles in the crumbs may remain cemented together and have a more lasting effect on soil structure. Too much ferric hydroxide can have a harmful effect because tightly cemented crumbs are very difficult to wet again after they have dried out.

This condition occurs in the so-called "drummy" soils found in the fen district.

Where there is very little organic matter or ferric hydroxide the stability of the crumbs depends mainly on the amount of clay present. The more clay there is, the stronger will be the forces holding the particles together.

Some soil structures are more stable than others, e.g. clays usually have a more stable structure than silts. Soils containing fine sand and silt easily lose their structure and are difficult to work if they are low in organic matter. This is because under wet conditions the sand and silty materials flow very easily and block the aeration and drainage channels in the soil.

Tilth is a term used to describe the condition of the soil in a seedbed. For example, the soil may be in a finely divided state or it may be rough and lumpy; also, the soil may be damp or it may be very dry. Whether a tilth is suitable or not partly depends on the crop to be grown. In general, small seeds require a finer tilth than large seeds.

Soil Fertility and Productivity

Soil fertility is a rather loose term used to indicate the potential capacity of a soil to grow a crop (or sequence of crops). The productivity of a soil is the combined result of fertility and management.

The fertility of a soil at any one time is partly due to its natural make-up (inherent or *natural fertility*) and partly due to its *condition* (variable fertility) at that time.

Natural fertility has an important influence on the *rental* and *sale value* of land. It is the result of factors which are normally beyond the control of the farmer, such as:

(1) the texture and chemical composition of the mineral matter,
(2) the topography (natural slope of the land)—this can affect drainage, temperature and workability of the soil,
(3) climate and local weather—particularly the effects on temperature, and rainfall (quantity and distribution).

Soil condition is largely dependent on the management of the soil in recent times. It can be built up by good husbandry but if this high standard is not maintained the soil will soon return to its natural fertility level. The application of fertilizers can raise soil fertility by increasing the quantities of plant food in the growth and decay cycle.

Management can control the following production factors:

(1) the amount of organic matter in the soil, (see "Soils"),
(2) artificial drainage and irrigation (see "Soil Improvement"),
(3) erosion (removal of soil by wind and water) (see "Claying"),
(4) pH of the soil (see liming), and the plant nutrients applied (see "Fertilizers" and "Crops"),
(5) cultivations and time of planting (see "Cultivations"),
(6) variety and plant spacing (see individual crops),
(7) sequence of cropping (see "Rotations"),
(8) weeds, pests and diseases (see separate chapters).

Good management of the above factors should maintain or increase soil fertility and at the same time be commercially profitable. These subjects are dealt with in more detail in other chapters.

Types of Soil

There are wide variations in the types of soil found on farms. They may be classified in various ways but here they are grouped according to texture. The amount of clay, silt and sand which they contain can be found by a mechanical analysis. This is an elaborate separation of the particles by settling from a water suspension and sieving in the laboratory which can give accurate measurements of the amount of sand, silt and clay particles present. Gravel and stones are not included in a sample for mechanical analysis. The generally accepted size of particles for each material is given in Table 1.

The "farm-soil" groups to be considered in more detail are: *Clay, sand, loam, silt, calcareous, peat* and *black fen.*

The approximate mechanical analyses of some soil types are shown in Table 2.

TABLE 1.

Material	Diameter of particles
Clay	less than 0·002 mm
Silt	0·02–0·002 mm
Fine sand	0·2–0·02 mm
Coarse sand	2·0–0·2 mm
Gravel	more than 2·0 mm

TABLE 2. TEXTURAL GROUPING OF SOILS (ON DRY WEIGHT)

Soil type	Texture	Clay (%)	Silt (%)	Sand (%)
Clay	Fine (heavy)	over 50	15–25	up to 35
Clay loam	Fine (heavy)	30–50	15–25	35–45
Silt loam	Medium	20–30	30–50	30–35
Loam	Medium	20–30	20–30	about 50
Sandy loam	Coarse (light)	10–20	15–25	55–75
Sand	Coarse (light)	0–10	0–10	80–100

A given amount of clay has a very much greater effect on the characteristics of a soil than the same amount of sand or silt.

CLAY SOILS

These soils have a high proportion of clay and silty material—usually over 60%; of this, at least half is *pure clay*, which is mainly responsible for their characteristic qualities. The particles of pure clay are so small that they cannot be seen under an ordinary microscope but they have several very important *colloidal* and base-exchange properties. e.g.

They are gluey and plastic (can be moulded).

They will *swell* when wetted and *shrink* when dried.

They can group together into small clusters (flocculate) or become scattered (deflocculated).

They can combine with various chemical substances (base-exchange) such as calcium, sodium, potassium and ammonia and in this way may hold plant nutrients in the soil.

Grouping or flocculation of the particles is very important in making clay soils easy to work. Clay particles combined with calcium (lime) will flocculate easily whereas those combined with sodium will not and so salt (sodium chloride) must be used very carefully on clay soils. Deflocculation can occur when clays are worked in a wet condition. The adhesive properties of clay are very beneficial to the soil structure when the groups of particles are small (like crumbs) but can be very harmful when large lumps (clods) are formed. Frost action, and alternating periods of wetting and drying will help to restore them to the flocculated condition.

Characteristics

(1) Clay soils feel very *sticky* when wet and can be moulded into various shapes.
(2) They can hold more water than other types and so are *drought-resistant*.
(3) They *lie wet in winter* so stock should be taken off the land to avoid *poaching*.
(4) They are very *late* in warming up in springtime because water heats up much slower than mineral matter.
(5) They are normally fairly *rich in potash*, but are deficient in phosphates.
(6) Lime requirements are very variable—a clay soil which is well limed usually has a better structure and so is easier to work; over-liming will not cause any troubles such as trace-element deficiency.

Management

They should not be worked in spring when wet because they become puddled and later dry into hard lumps, which can only be broken down by well timed cultivations following repeated wetting

c

(swelling) and drying (shrinking). Some air is drawn into cracks caused by shrinkage, and remains when the clod is wetted again and so lines of weakness are formed which eventually allow the clod to be broken. In dry weather irrigation may be used to wet the clods.

In prolonged dry weather, wide and deep cracks are formed which may break animals legs but which are very beneficial for drainage later.

Clays are often called *heavy* soils because, compared with light (sandy) soils, for ploughing and cultivating two to four times the amount of tractor power is required. All cultivations must be very carefully timed (often restricted to a short period) so that the soil structure is not damaged. This means that more tractors and implements are required than on similar sized loam or sandy soil farms. Autumn ploughing, to allow for a frost tilth, is essential if good seed-beds are to be produced in the spring.

Good drainage is essential. Many clay fields are still in "ridge-and-furrow". This was set up by ploughing—making the "openings" and "finishes" in the same respective places until a distinct ridge and furrow pattern was formed. The direction of the furrows is the same as the fall on the field so that water can easily run off into ditches. This practice also increases the grazing area of a field and for this reason is sometimes found on other types of soil! If these ridges and furrows are levelled out then a mole-drainage system using tiled main drains should be substituted (see "Drainage"). This change is well worthwhile where arable crops are grown.

In many clay-land areas—especially where rainfall is high—the fields are often small and irregular in shape because the boundaries were originally ditches which followed the fall of the land. The hedges and deciduous trees, which were planted later, grow very well on these fertile, wet soils.

The close texture and an adequate water supply often restrict root development on clay soils.

Organic matter, such as strawy farmyard manure, ploughed-in straw or grassland make these soils easier to work.

Cropping

Because of the many difficulties to be overcome in growing arable crops on these soils they are often left in *permanent grass* and only grazed during the growing season. Where arable crops are grown, a 3- or 4-year ley is often included in the rotation. *Winter wheat* is the most popular arable crop; *winter beans* are also grown in some areas. Both these crops are planted in the autumn (preferably October) when more liberties can be taken with seed-bed preparation than would be permissible in the springtime. *Mangolds* and *cabbage* grow well on clay soils but are declining in popularity in many areas. *Sugar-beet* and *potatoes* are grown in some districts but are very troublesome because of the difficulties in seed-bed preparation, weed control and harvesting—especially in a wet autumn. The best place to take either of these crops is after a period under grass when the soil structure is more stable and the soil easier to work.

SANDY SOILS

Characteristics

(1) In many ways these are the opposite of clays and are often called *light* soils because comparatively little power is required to draw cultivation implements.

(2) They can be worked at any time—even in wet weather—without harmful effects.

(3) They are normally free-draining but a few drains may be required where there is clay or other impervious layer underneath.

(4) They have a high proportion of sand and other coarse particles but very little clay—usually less than 5%—(they feel gritty).

(5) They warm up early in spring but crops are very liable to "burn-up" in a dry period because the water holding capacity is low.

Management

Sandy soils are naturally very low in plant nutrients and fertilizers are easily washed out, so adequate amounts of fertilizer must
be applied to every crop. *Liming* is necessary but must be used
carefully—a little and often is the rule here.

Organic matter—especially as *humus*—is very beneficial because
it helps to hold water and plant nutrients in the soil. On properly
limed fields it breaks down very rapidly because the soil micro-
organisms are very active in these open-textured soils which have
a good air supply.

Irrigation can be very important if the rainfall is low or not well
distributed over the growing season.

In some sandy areas the surface soil is liable to "blow" in dry,
windy weather and so could destroy a young crop. Where possible,
the remedy is to add about 150 tons/acre of clay (see "Claying").
Shelter belts are helpful where clay is not readily available.

Cropping

A wide range of crops can be grown but yields are very dependent
on a good supply of water and adequate fertilizers. *Market gardening*
is often carried on where a good sandy area is situated near a large
population; e.g. Sandy, Potton, Biggleswade area (Beds.). Here
growers are prepared to use irrigation and apply plenty of manures
and fertilizers on these *very early, easily worked soils.*

On the lighter sands in low rainfall areas and where irrigation is
not possible, the main crops grown are *rye, carrots, sugar-beet,* and
lucerne; lupins are grown in a few areas where the soil is very poor
and acid.

On the better sandy soils, and particularly where the water supply
(from rain or irrigation) is reasonably good, the main arable farm-
crops grown are *barley, peas, rye, sugar-beet, potatoes* and *carrots.*

Because of the poor quality of this type of land the farms and
fields are usually larger than on better-land farms. Hedges are not
very common because there is not enough water for good growth.
The trees are usually drought-resistant coniferous types.

Stock can be out-wintered on sandy soils with very little risk of damage by poaching even in wet weather.

LOAMS

Characteristics

(1) These are intermediate in texture between the clays and sandy soils and, in general, have most of the advantages and few of the disadvantages of these two extreme types. They may feel gritty but also somewhat sticky.

(2) The amount of clay present varies considerably and so this group is sometimes divided into *heavy* or *clay loams* (resembling clays in many respects), *medium loams* and *sandy* or *light loams* (resembling the better sandy soils).

(3) These soils warm up reasonably early in spring and are fairly resistant to drought.

Management

Loams are easily worked but should not be worked when wet—especially clay loams. They usually require to be drained but this is not difficult using tile or plastic drains.

Cropping

They are regarded by most farmers as the *best all-round soils* because they are naturally fertile and can be used for growing any crop provided the depth of soil is sufficient. Crop yields do not vary much from year to year.

Farms with loamy soils can be used for most types of arable or grassland farming but in general, mixed farming is carried on. Cereals, potatoes and sugar-beet are the main cash crops and leys provide grazing and winter bulk foods for dairy cows, beef cattle or sheep.

CALCAREOUS SOILS

Characteristics

These are soils derived from *chalk* and *limestone* rocks and contain various amounts of calcium carbonate—usually 5–50%. The depth of soil and subsoil may vary from 3 in. to over 3 ft. In general, the deep soils are more fertile than the shallow ones. The ease of working and stickiness of these soils depends on the amount of clay and chalk or limestone present; they usually have a loamy texture. Sharp-edged *flints* of various sizes, found in soils over-lying some of the chalk formations, are very wearing on cultivation implements and rubber tyres, and are rather destructive when picked up by harvesting machinery. In some places the flints are found mixed with clay, e.g. *clay-with-flints* soils.

The soils are free-draining except in a few small areas where there is a deep clayish subsoil. Dry valleys are characteristic of these downlands and wolds. The few rivers rise from underground streams.

There are very few hedges and most of the trees have been planted for various reasons—they are mainly beech and conifers.

Walls of local stone form the field boundaries in some limestone areas, e.g. the Cotswolds.

Management

The soils are usually deficient in phosphates and potash but only the deeper ones are likely to need liming. (see "Liming".) Organic matter can be beneficial but it breaks down fairly rapidly and may be expensive to replace.

The farms and fields on this type of land are usually large— especially on the thinner soils.

Some areas are still unfenced and have no water laid on for stock but this state of affairs is changing as mixed farming systems with grazing animals replace the folded-sheep flocks.

The flooding of water-meadows used to be a common practice but is not done now because labour costs are too high.

CROPPING

Barley and *wheat* (on the deeper soils) are the best crops for these soils. The combine-drill for sowing cereals has been very useful in producing good crops—particularly on the poorer, thinner soils. Continuous barley growing is now common on many farms and is likely to become a widely accepted practice. Roots, such as *sugar-beet* and *mangolds*, and *potatoes* are grown on some of the deeper soils. *Leys* for grazing and seed production provide a rotational break with cereal growing. *Kale* is grown on some farms for stock, and pheasant cover! Apart from some parkland, only the poorest, thinnest soils remain as permanent grassland.

SILTS

Characteristics

These are soils which contain a high proportion of silt (up to 80% or more). The particles (between clay and sand in size) pack together very closely and retard the movement of water.

Bad drainage is one of the main problems with these soils. They do not have a stable subsoil structure such as is found in clay soils. The particles do not group together readily and firmly and so quickly block up drainage cracks and tile drains. Unlike clay, the silt particles cannot take part in chemical reactions so adding lime is not helpful; it is very difficult to create an easy-working soil structure. Frost has very little useful effect.

Management and cropping

Arable cropping is very difficult and these areas are best left down to permanent grass. Deep-rooted plants, such as *lucerne*, left growing for several years, are likely to be helpful in opening up the subsoil with their roots and so facilitating drainage.

There is not much land of this type in the British Isles—the best example is part of the Lower Weald in Sussex.

Note. The Fenland "silts" are alluvial material consisting mainly of clay, silt and fine sand. They vary in texture from sandy to medium loam. These soils are very fertile and fairly easy to work. They are cropped intensively with all kinds of arable crops— the main ones are *wheat, potatoes, sugar-beet, peas, seed production from root crops and grasses, bulbs* and *market gardening crops.*

PEATS AND PEATY SOILS

Characteristics

Peaty soils contain about 20–25% of organic matter whereas there is about 50–90% in true peats.

The *acid* or *peat-bog* peats and peaty soils have been formed in waterlogged areas where plants such as mosses, cotton grass, heather, molinia and rushes grew. The dead material from these plants was only partly broken down by the types of bacteria which can survive under these acidic waterlogged conditions. This "humus" material built up slowly—probably a foot or so every century.

When reclaimed, these soils break down easily to release nutrients, particularly nitrogen, but they are very low in phosphates and potash. Old tree trunks have to be dug out from time to time as the level of the soil falls due to organic matter break down.

Management

Before reclaiming this land for cropping, much of the peat is often cut away for fuel or sold as peat moss for horticultural purposes or bedding. Good drainage must then be carried out by cutting deep ditches through the area. Deep ploughing also helps to drain the soil. Heavy applications (up to 10 tons/acre) of ground limestone may be required to neutralize the acidity

In the first year, about 5 tons/acre of farmyard manure improves the yields of pioneer crops (usually potatoes, sometimes oats or rye); the reason for this may be that the F.Y.M. introduces beneficial types of bacteria.

Cropping

In exposed areas they are often sown down to good grasses and clovers. Good swards can be established but these must not be over-grazed or "poached" in wet weather otherwise the field will quickly go back to rushes and weed grasses. Under cultivation, most arable crops can be grown but potatoes and oats are the most suitable.

BLACK FEN SOILS

Characteristics

Black Fen soils are found in part of the Fen district of East Anglia and are amongst the most fertile soils in the British Isles. (The "muck soils" of North America are somewhat similar.)

These soils were formed in marshy river estuary conditions where the water came from limestone and chalk areas and so carried calcium carbonate and, in flood times, considerable amounts of silty material. The remains of the vegetation (mainly reeds, sedges and other estuary plants) did not break down completely because of the waterlogged conditions and so built up as humus. The soils vary a lot from district to district but most of them consist almost entirely of organic matter.

Management

After building strong sea walls; the area has been reclaimed by draining with deep ditches and underground drains. Most of the land is below sea level and so the water in the ditches has to be pumped over the sea walls or into the main drainage channels.

The soil breaks down readily and the level is falling about 1 in. per year and eventually will reach the clay or gravel subsoil. Tree trunks have to be dug out from time to time.

"Blowing" in spring is a serious problem on these dry, sooty black, friable soils. Several plantings of crop seedlings together with the top 2 or 3 in. of soil and fertilizers may be blown into the ditches. This can be prevented by applying 150–300 tons of clay per acre (see "Claying"), or by deep ploughing (3–5 ft. deep) to mix the underlying clay and organic top soil.

These soils are rich in nitrogen, released by the break down of the organic matter, but are very poor in phosphates and potash and also trace elements such as manganese and copper.

Cropping

This is an intensive arable area where the main crops are *wheat*, *potatoes* and *sugar-beet;* also smaller acreages of *celery, peas, carrots* and market garden crops.

In some parts leys have been introduced—with limited success—in an attempt to check the rapid rate of breakdown of the soils.

Soil Improvement

1. LIMING

Most farm crops will not grow satisfactorily if the soil is very acid (sour). This can be remedied by applying one of the commonly used liming materials.

Soil reaction

All substances in the presence of water are either acid, alkaline or neutral. The term *reaction* describes the degree or condition of acidity, alkalinity or neutrality. Acidity and alkalinity are expressed by a pH scale on which pH 7 is neutral, numbers below 7 indicate acidity and those above 7 alkalinity. Most cultivated soils have a pH range between 4·5 and 8·0 and may be grouped as follows:

pH	Reaction
Over 7	Alkaline
7	Neutral
6·0–6·9	Slightly acid
5·2–5·9	Moderately acid
Below 5·2	Very acid

Lime requirement

This is the amount of lime required to raise the pH to approximately 6·5 in the top layer of soil (6 in.). This amount varies considerably with the degree of acidity or "sourness", and the type of soil. Heavy (clay) soils and soils rich in organic matter require more lime to raise the pH than other types of soil. For example, to raise the pH from 5·5 to 6·5 on a sandy loam may require about 2 tons/acre of ground limestone, but on a clay soil 4–5 tons/acre of ground limestone may be required. The actual lime requirement can be calculated from chemical tests in the laboratory. It is unnecessary to lime soils which have a pH of more than 6·5.

Indications of soil acidity (i.e. a need for liming)

(a) Crops failing in patches—particularly the acid-sensitive ones such as *barley* and *sugar-beet*. The plants usually die off or are very unthrifty in the seedling stage.

(b) On grassland, there are poor types of grasses present such as *bents*. Often a *mat* of undecayed vegetation builds up because the acidity reduces the activities of earthworms and bacteria which break down such material.

(c) On arable land, weeds such as *sheep's sorrel, corn marigold* and *spurrey* are common.

(d) *Soil analysis.* Chemical and electrical methods may be used to determine the pH and lime requirements of a soil. Portable testing equipment, using colour charts, are sometimes used to test for pH.

The main benefits of applying lime are:

(1) It neutralizes the acidity or sourness.

(2) It supplies calcium (and sometimes magnesium) for plant nutrition.

(3) It improves soil structure. In well limed soils, plants usually produce more roots and grow better; bacteria are more active in breaking down organic matter. This usually results in a better soil structure and the soil can be cultivated more easily (see also "Soil Structure").

(4) It affects the availability of plant nutrients. The main plant nutrients such as nitrogen, phosphates and potash are freely available on properly limed soils. Too much lime in the soil is likely to make some minor nutrients unavailable to plants, e.g. *manganese, boron, copper* and *zinc*—this is least likely to happen in clay soils.

pH and crop growth. To give crops the best opportunity to grow well the soil pH should be near or above the following.

	pH
Barley, sugar-beet and lucerne	6·5
Red clover	6·0
Wheat, beans, peas, turnips and swedes	5·5
Oats, potatoes	5·0
Rye and lupins	4·5

Lime is removed from the soil by:

(1) *Drainage.* Lime is fairly easily removed in drainage water. 1–15 cwt/acre of calcium carbonate may be lost annually. The rate of loss is greatest in industrial, smoke polluted areas, areas of high rainfall, well drained soils and soils rich in lime.

(2) *Fertilizers and manures.* Every 1 cwt of sulphate of ammonia removes about 1 cwt of calcium carbonate from the soil. Poultry manure may also remove some lime.

(3) *Crops.* Varying amounts of lime are removed in this way, for example:

Cereals	2–6lb calcium carbonate per ton of grain.
	12–16 lb calcium carbonate per ton of straw.
Potatoes	15 lb calcium carbonate per 10 tons of tubers.
Sugar-beet	50 lb calcium carbonate per 15 tons of roots.
	200 lb calcium carbonate per 13 tons of tops.
Swedes	90 lb calcium carbonate per 25 tons of roots.
Kale (carted off)	400 lb calcium carbonate per 22 tons of crop.
Lucerne Hay	500 lb calcium carbonate per 4 tons hay.

(4) *Stock* also remove lime, for example, a 10 cwt bullock sold off the farm removes about 36 lb of calcium carbonate in its bones. A 100 lb lamb about 3 lb of calcium carbonate and 1000 gal of milk about 35 lb of calcium carbonate.

Materials commonly used for liming soils

Ground limestone or chalk (also called carbonate of lime and calcium carbonate, $CaCO_3$).

This is obtained by quarrying the limestone or chalk rock and grinding it to a fine powder. It is the commonest liming material used at present.

Burnt lime (also called quicklime, lump lime, shell lime and calcium oxide, CaO). This is produced by burning lumps of limestone or chalk rock with coke or other fuel in a kiln. Carbon dioxide is given off and the lumps of burnt lime which are left are sold as lumps, or are ground up ready for mechanical spreading. This "concentrated" form of lime is especially useful for application to remote areas where transport costs are high. Burnt lime may scorch growing crops because it readily takes water from the leaves. When lumps of burnt lime are wetted they break down to a fine powder called *hydrated* or *slaked lime* [$Ca(OH)_2$].

Hydrated lime is a good liming material but is usually too expensive for liming the soil.

Waste limes. These are liming materials which can sometimes be obtained from industrial processes where lime is used as a purifying material. These limes are cheap but usually contain a lot of water. Some of the sources are: sugar-beet factories, waste from manufacture of sulphate of ammonia, soap works, bleaching, tanneries, etc. Care is needed when using these materials because some may contain harmful substances.

A comparison of the various liming materials is as follows:
1 ton *burnt lime* (CaO) is equivalent to

27 cwt *hydrated lime* $Ca(OH)_2$

or 36 cwt *ground limestone* $CaCO_3$

or at least 50 cwt waste lime (usually $CaCO_3$)

The supplier of lime must give a statement of the *neutralizing value* (N.V.) of the liming material—this is really the same as the calcium oxide equivalent.

Magnesium or dolomitic limestone. This limestone consists of magnesium carbonate ($MgCO_3$) and $CaCO_3$ and is commonly used as a liming material in areas where it is found. Magnesium carbonate has a better neutralizing value (about one-fifth better) than calcium carbonate. In addition, the magnesium may prevent magnesium deficiency diseases in crops (e.g. interveinal yellowing of leaves in potatoes, sugar-beet, oats) and stock (e.g. "grass-staggers" in grazing animals).

Cost. The cost of liming is largely dependent on the transport costs from the lime works to the farm. By dividing the cost per ton of the liming material by the figure for the neutralizing value, the *unit cost* is obtained. In this way it is possible to compare the costs of various liming materials. About two-thirds of the cost of liming is paid by government subsidy.

Most farmers now use ground limestone or chalk and arrange for it to be spread mechanically by the suppliers. Where large amounts are required (over 3 tons/acre) it is sometimes best to apply it in two dressings, e.g. half before ploughing and half after ploughing.

Rates of application

1–10 tons/acre of calcium carbonate ($CaCO_3$) or its equivalent may be needed to satisfy the lime requirements of a soil. Afterwards, about $1-1\frac{1}{2}$ tons $CaCO_3$ per acre every 4 years should be enough to replace average losses.

2. DRAINAGE (SEE ALSO "WATER IN THE SOIL")

Normally, the soil can only hold some of the rainwater which falls on it. The remainder either runs off or is evaporated from the surface or soaks through the soil to the subsoil. If surplus water is prevented from moving through the soil and subsoil it soon fills up all the pore-spaces and this will kill or stunt the crops growing there.

The *water-table* is the level in the soil or subsoil below which all the pore space is filled with water. This is not easy to see or measure in clay soils but can be seen in open textured soils (see Fig. 27). The water-table level fluctuates through the year and in

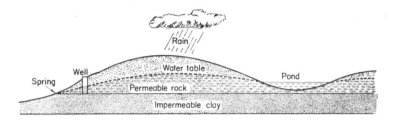

FIG. 27. Diagram showing position of a water-table and its effect on the water levels in the well and pond.

the British Isles is usually highest in February and lowest in September; the greater amount of evaporation, much more transpiration and lower rainfall (usually) in summer allow the level to fall in late summer and early autumn. This is shown by the water level falling in ponds and shallow wells, some springs drying up and wet parts of fields drying out.

In chalk and limestone areas, and in most sandy and gravelly soils, water can drain away easily into the porous subsoil. These are *free-draining* soils.

On most other types of farmland some sort of artificial *field drainage* is necessary to carry away the surplus water and so keep the water-table at a reasonable level. For most arable farm crops the water-table should be about 2 ft or more below the surface; for grassland 1–1½ ft is sufficient.

Some of the signs of bad drainage are:

(a) Machinery is easily "bogged down" in wet weather.
(b) Stock grazing pastures in wet weather easily damage and trample holes in the sward (poaching).
(c) Water lies about in pools on the surface for many days after heavy rain.

(d) Weeds such as rushes, sedges, horsetail, tussock grass and meadowsweet are common in grassland. Peat forms in places which have been very wet for a long time.

(e) Young plants are pale green or yellow in colour and unthrifty, when compared with the greener and more vigorous plants on drier land nearby.

(f) Subsoil is often various shades of blue, or grey compared with shades of reddish brown, yellow and orange in well drained soil.

Some of the practical advantages of good drainage are:

(a) Well drained land is better aerated and the crops grow better and are less likely to be damaged by root-decaying fungi.

(b) The soil dries out better in spring and so warms up quicker and can be worked early.

(c) Plants are encouraged to form a deeper and more extensive root system. In this way they can often obtain more plant food.

(d) Grassland is firmer—especially after wet periods. It is often possible to safely out-winter stock on well drained land without risk of poaching. Rushes and other moisture-loving weeds usually disappear.

(e) Disease risk from parasites is reduced. A good example is the liver fluke—this must pass part of its life cycle in a water snail found on badly drained land.

(f) Inter-row cultivations and harvesting of root crops and potatoes can be carried out more efficiently.

(g) Fertilizers and manures will give better results because the crop can grow more vigorously.

The main methods used to control the water-table level are:

(a) Open channels or ditches.

(b) Tile drains (underground).

(c) Mole drains (underground).

(d) Modified mole drains using plastic strips or tubes of various kinds (new development).

Ditches and open drains

Ditches may be adequate to drain an area by themselves but they usually serve as outlets for underground drains. They are capable of dealing with large volumes of water in very wet periods. The size of a ditch varies according to the area it serves (see Fig. 28). Ditches

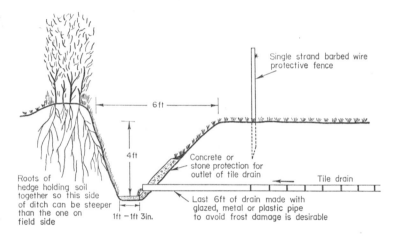

FIG. 28. Section through a typical field ditch and tile drain.

should be kept cleaned out to their original depth as often as necessary—usually annually or biennially. The spoil removed should be spread well clear of the edge of the ditch. Many different types of machines are now available for making new ditches and cleaning neglected ones.

Small open channels 10–60 yd apart are used for draining hill grazing areas. These are either dug by hand using a special spade or made with a special type of plough, drawn by a crawler tractor. Similar open channels are used on low lying meadow land where underground drainage is not possible.

Underground drains—tile drainage

The distance between drains which is necessary for good drainage depends on the soil texture. In clay soils the small pore spaces restrict the movement of water and so the drains must be spaced much closer together than on the lighter types of soil where water can flow freely through the large pore spaces (see Figs. 29 and 30).

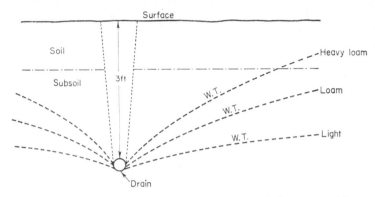

FIG. 29. Diagram to show how the steepness of the water-table (W.T.) varies with different types of soil.

The ideal spacing for underground drains is set out below.

Soil type	Depth of drains (ft)	Distance between drains (yd)
Clay	2 –2½	3– 7
Loam	2½–3	7–10
Sandy	3 –4	10–15
Peat	at least 3½	6–10

In practice, the drains are usually spaced further apart to reduce the cost of the work.

Tile drainage is the commonest type of underground drainage. It can be used on all types of soil but on clay soils it is usually restricted to main drains only because of the high cost. Tiles are made of burnt clay, but sometimes pipes made of concrete are used. They are usually 1 ft. long and of various diameters. $2\frac{1}{2}$–3 in. diameter tiles are used for the ordinary side or lateral drains: 4, 6 and 9 in. diameter tiles are used for the main drains. The size of tile required will depend on the rainfall, area to be drained, fall, and soil structure.

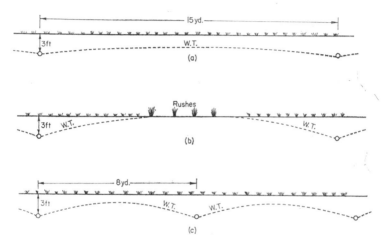

FIG. 30. Diagram showing the effect of spacing of drains on the water table (W.T.) (a) light (sandy) soil, (b) and (c) heavy loam soils.

When tile drainage is used on clays and heavy loam soils, a porous material such as gravel or clinker should be used as backfill to allow the water to move down to the tiles easily. The cost of this material is reduced when narrow trenches are dug for the tiles.

There are many types of trenching and tile laying machines available. Most tile drainage work is done by specialist contractors.

Mole drainage

This is a cheap drainage method which can be used in some fields. Although the method is sometimes used on peat soils it is normally used in fields which have:

(a) *clay subsoil* (no stones, sand or gravel patches),

(b) *suitable fall* (2–14 in./chain),

(c) *reasonably smooth surface.*

A mole plough, which has a torpedo or bullet shaped "mole" attached to a steel coulter or blade, forms a cylindrical channel in the subsoil. The three main types are:

(1) mounted on three-point linkage,

(2) on wheeled carrying frame and adjustable for depth by winch,

(3) simple skid type (see Fig. 31).

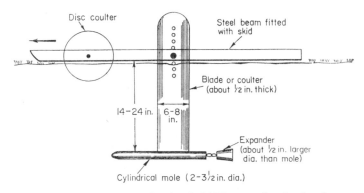

FIG. 31. Diagram of a simple (skid) type of mole plough.

The best conditions for mole draining are when the subsoil is damp enough to be plastic and forms a good surface on the mole channel, and also sufficiently dry to form cracks as the mole plough passes (see Fig. 32). If the surface is dry the tractor hauling the plough can get a better grip. The plough should be drawn slowly (about 2 m.p.h.) otherwise the vacuum created is likely to spoil the mole. Reasonably dry weather after moling will allow the surface of the mole to harden and so it should last longer.

Mole drains are drawn 3-5 yd apart except on "ridge and furrow" land where one or more drains are drawn along the furrows. For best results the moles should be drawn through the porous

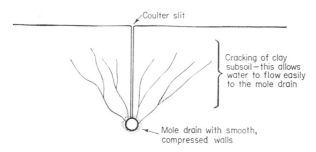

Coulter slit

Cracking of clay
subsoil — this allows
water to flow easily
to the mole drain

Mole drain with smooth,
compressed walls

FIG. 32. Section through a mole drain and surrounding soil.

back filling of a tiled main drain ("tile-cum-mole" system (see
Figs. 33 and 34)). 1½–2 chains of tiled main are usually required
per acre. The tiled main is semi-permanent and a new set of mole
drains can be drawn every 5–15 years as required. A large wheeled
tractor can pull a 2 in. mole 14–18 in. deep. For larger and deeper
drains a crawler tractor is required.

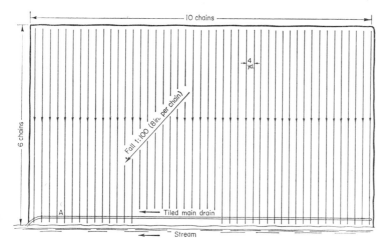

10 chains

4 yd.

6 chains

Fall 1:100 (8 in. per chain)

A   Tiled main drain

Stream

FIG. 33. Layout of mole drainage (with tiled main) in a six-acre
field. Section through drains A shown in Fig. 34.

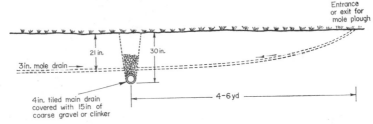

FIG. 34. Section through tile drain shown in Fig. 33 to show how water from the mole drain can enter the tile drain through the porous backfilling.

New developments

Experiments are now going on to test out new methods of drainage which will be cheaper than the present tile system. An interesting development is the use of perforated plastic strips which are drawn into the soil by a modified mole plough. The strips are formed into a cylindrical lining for the mole drain. This type of drain could be used on most types of soil.

A further modification is the use of a hollow coulter on the mole plough which allows a porous filling to be put into the coulter slit.

Polythene tubing (2 in. diameter and perforated with numerous small slots) is now available in 10 chain lengths supplied as large coils. It can be laid by modified mole poughs or trenching machines.

Plastic pipes, 20 ft long and 2 in. in diameter with 1 in. transverse slits spaced 2 in. apart are now being used instead of 3 in. tile drains. They are very light compared with tiles and can be laid by modified tile laying machines.

3. IRRIGATION (SEE ALSO "WATER IN THE SOIL")

Irrigation can be used to supply water to crops which are suffering from drought. If water is not applied at such times then the crops are checked and may die. This means low yields and the quality may be poor.

Irrigation water, like rainfall, is usually measured in inches (1 in./acre = 101 tons or 22,460 gal. of water).

To grow satisfactorily, most crops in the British Isles will require the following amounts of water if their leaves are covering the ground:

1 in. every 14–16 days in April and September,
1 in. every 10–12 days in May and August,
1 in. every 7– 8 days in June and July.

For best results, this must be evenly spread over the growing season—especially on the lighter types of soil. Clay and silt and soils rich in organic matter can hold more reserves of water and so are not so dependent on even distribution. The approximate amounts of available water which various soils can hold are shown in Table 3.

TABLE 3.

Soil type	Amount of *available* water (approx.) per foot depth of soil (in.)
Sandy	$\frac{3}{4}$–1
Loams and silts	$2\frac{1}{2}$–3
Clays	2 –$2\frac{1}{2}$
Fen	3 –4

The amount of organic matter in the soil can alter the water-holding capacity very considerably (see "Organic Matter"). The subsoil usually has a lower capacity than the soil.

The greatest need for irrigation in the British Isles is in the south-east, where the lower rainfall and higher potential evaporation and transpiration means that irrigation would be beneficial about 9 years out of 10. In the wetter western and northern areas the need is much less.

In many parts of this country very limited amounts of water are available for irrigation although much could be done to improve this situation by the construction of reservoirs to conserve the winter surplus. Grants are available for permanent works of this kind.

More experimental work is required to determine the stages of growth at which crops are most responsive to irrigation and also minimum water requirements, for example:

It is known that peas are most responsive at "start of flowering" and "pod swelling" stages.

Also, if a maincrop potato variety which normally produces a lot of tubers (e.g. King Edward) is irrigated before the tubers are marble size too many small tubers and a low ware yield may result.

Irrigation of sugar-beet before the leaves meet across the rows encourages surface root development instead of deep rooting which would be less dependent on irrigation.

Table 4 is a useful guide to the rate at which various soils can absorb water and so the rate at which irrigation water should be applied.

TABLE 4.

Soil type	Time required to absorb 1 in. water (hr)	Depth of soil (at wilting point) which is wetted by 1 in. water (in.)
Sandy	1–2	15–18
Loams	3	5–10
Clay	4–5	4– 8

Irrigation water is applied by:

(a) *Rotary sprinklers.* These provide a very common method nowadays. Each rotating sprinkler covers an area about 70–90 ft in diameter.

(b) *Rain guns.* These are used on grassland and crops such as sugar-beet which are covering the ground. The droplets are large. Diameter of area covered may be 200–400 ft. Some types are used for organic irrigation (slurry).

(c) *Spraylines.* These apply the water gently and are used mainly for horticultural crops.

(d) *Surface channels.* This method requires almost level or contoured land. It is wasteful of land, water and labour.

(e) *Underground pipes.* On level land, water can be dammed in the ditches and allowed to flow up the drainage pipes into the subsoil and lower soil layers. This is drainage in reverse!

4. WARPING

This is a process of soil formation where land, lying between high and low water levels, alongside a tidal river, is deliberately flooded with muddy water. The area to be treated is surrounded by earth banks fitted with sluice gates. At high tide, water is allowed to flood quickly onto the enclosed area and is run off slowly through sluice gates at low tide. The fineness of the material deposited will depend on the length of time allowed for settling—the coarse particles will settle very quickly but the finer particles may take one or more days to settle. The depth of the deposit may be 18 in. in one winter. When enough alluvium is deposited it is then drained and prepared for cropping. Sections dug through the subsoil clearly show separate deposition layers.

These soils are very fertile and are usually intensively cropped with arable crops such as *potatoes, sugar-beet, peas, wheat* and *barley*.

Part of the land around the Humber estuary is warpland, and the best is probably that in the lower Trent valley. Most of this work was done last century.

5. CLAYING

The texture of "blow-away" sandy soils and black fen soils can be improved by applying 100–300 tons/acre of clay or marl (a lime-rich clay). If the subsoil of the area is clay this can be dug out of trenches and roughly scattered by a dragline excavator. In other cases the clay is dug in pits and transported in special lorry spreaders. Rotary cultivators help to spread the clay. If the work is done in late summer or autumn, the winter frosts help to break down the lumps of clay.

Tillage and Cultivations

Cultivations are field operations which attempt to alter the soil structure. The main object is to provide a suitable seed-bed in which a crop can be planted and will grow satisfactorily; sometimes cultivations are used to kill weeds, or bury the remains of previous crops. The timing of cultivations—particularly with regard to the weather and on the heavier soils—is more an art than a science and is largely based on experience. The cost of the work can be considerably reduced by good timing and use of the right implements. Ideally, a good seed-bed should be prepared with the minimum amount of working and the least loss of moisture. On heavy soil and in a wet season, some loss of moisture is sometimes desirable. On the medium and heavy soils full advantage should be taken of weathering effects; for example, ploughing in the autumn will allow frost to break the soil into a crumb structure; wetting and drying alternately will have a similar effect.

SEED-BED REQUIREMENTS FOR VARIOUS CROPS

(1) *Cereals*

(a) *Autumn planted.* The objects here is to provide a tilth (seed-bed condition) which consists of fine material and lumps about fist-size. It should allow for the seed to be drilled and easily covered and the surface should remain rough after planting. The lumps on the surface will prevent the heavier soils from "capping" easily in a mild wet winter and they also protect the base of the cereals from the harmful effects of very cold winds. Harrowing and/or rolling may be done in the spring to break up a soil cap which may have formed and to firm the soil around plants which have been heaved by frost action.

(b) *Spring planted.* A fairly fine seed-bed is required in the springtime (very fine if grasses and clovers are to be undersown). If the seed-bed is dry or very loose after drilling it should be consolidated by rolling—this is especially important if the crop is undersown and where the soil is stony.

(2) *Root crops*, e.g. sugar-beet, swedes, and carrots: also *kale*. These crops have small seeds and so the seed-bed must be as fine as possible, level, and firm. This is particularly important when precision drills and very low seed rates (to reduce seed and thinning costs) are used. Good, early, ploughing with uniform, well packed and broken furrow slices will considerably reduce the amount of work required in the spring. If possible, deep cultivations should be avoided in the springtime so keeping frost mould on top and leaving unweathered soil well below the surface. Roots are usually sown on ridges in the higher rainfall areas; this avoids damage by surface water and also makes singling and harvesting easier.

(3) *Direct seeding of grasses and clovers*. Same as for roots.

(4) *Beans and peas*. Similar to cereals—but tilth need not be so fine. Peas grown on light soils may be drilled into the ploughed surface (or after one stroke of the harrow) if the ploughing has been well done.

(5) *Potatoes*. This crop is usually planted in ridges about 2–2½ ft wide and so deep cultivations are necessary. The fineness of tilth required depends on how the crop will be managed after planting. A fairly rough, damp seed-bed is usually preferable to a fine, dry tilth which has been worked too much. Most crops are worked many times after planting—such as harrowing down the ridges, ridging-up again, deep cultivations between the ridges and final earthing-up. The main object of these cultivations is to control weeds but the implements often damage the roots of the potato plants.

Most annual weeds can be controlled by spraying the ridges when the potato sprouts start to appear. This can replace most of the inter-row cultivations and reduce the number of clods produced by the rubber-tyred tractor wheels.

RECENT DEVELOPMENTS

The introduction of chemicals such as *paraquat* which can kill off grass swards and some grass weeds has led to the development of a new seeding technique. It is now possible to drill crops such as cereals and kale into killed-off grass turf or stubble without previous cultivations. The special drills used for this purpose can penetrate hard soil and sow the seed (and fertilizer) satisfactorily.

At present, the main problem to be overcome is the build up of surface trash which sometimes occurs around the drill coulters. Also, before full advantage can be taken of this system of cropping, effective herbicides must be found to give good control of such troublesome weeds as couch, field bindweed, coltsfoot and corn mint.

With the possible exception of light soils, this technique would not be suitable for crops such as sugar-beet or potatoes because the soil below the surface layer would be too firm to allow for normal development of the sugar-beet roots and potato tubers. Also, harvesting would be very difficult.

TILLAGE IMPLEMENTS

The main implements used for tillage are:

Ploughs. Ploughing is the first operation in seed-bed preparation on most farms and is likely to remain so for some time yet, although many farmers are now using rotary cultivators, heavy cultivators with fixed or spring tines, and mechanically driven digging or pulverizing machines, as alternatives to the plough. Good ploughing is probably the best method of burying weeds and the remains of previous crops; it can also set up the soil so that good frost penetration is possible. Fast ploughing produces a more broken furrow slice than slow steady work. The *mounted* or *semi-mounted plough* is replacing the *trailed type* on most farms because of ease of handling. *General purpose mouldboards* are commonly used; the shorter *digger* types (concave mouldboards) break the furrow slices better and are often used on the lighter soils. *Deep digger ploughs* are used where deep ploughing is required, e.g. for roots or potatoes. The *one-way* (*reversible*) type of plough is fairly popular for crops such as roots and peas: it has right-hand and left-hand mouldboards and no openings or finishes have to be made when ploughing so the seed-bed can be kept level. *Round-and-round* ploughing with the ordinary plough has almost the same effect although this is not a suitable method on all fields.

The proper use of skim and disc coulters and careful setting of the plough for depth, width and pitch can greatly improve the quality of the ploughing. The furrow slice can only be turned over satisfactorily if the depth is less than about two-thirds the width; the usual widths of ordinary plough bodies vary from 8 to 14 in. If possible, it is desirable to vary the depth of ploughing from year to year to avoid the formation of a plough pan. Very deep ploughing which brings up several inches of poorly weathered subsoil must be undertaken with care: the long term effects will probably be worthwhile but for a few years afterwards the soil may be rather sticky and difficult to work. Buried weed seeds, such as wild oats which have fallen down cracks, may be brought to the surface and may spoil the following crops. *"Chisel ploughing"* is a modern term used to describe the work done by a heavy duty cultivator with special spring or fixed tines—it does not move or invert all the soil as the ordinary plough does. *Disc* ploughs have large saucer-shaped discs instead of shares and mouldboards. Compared with the ordinary mouldboard ploughs they do not cut all the ground or invert the soil so well but they can work in harder and stickier soil conditions. They are more popular in dry countries. Double mouldboard *ridging* ploughs are used for potatoes and some root crops in the wetter areas.

Cultivators. These are tined implements which are used to break up the soil clods, (to ploughing depth). Some have tines which are rigid or are held by very strong springs which only give when an obstruction such as a strong tree root is struck. Others have spring tines which are constantly moving according to the resistance of the soil—they have a very good pulverizing effect and can often be pulled at a high speed; they can be useful for dragging the rhizomes of weeds, such as couch, to the surface. The shares on the tines may be of various widths. The pitch of the tines draws the implement into the soil. Depth can be controlled by tractor linkage or wheels. The timing of cultivations is very important if the operation is to be effective.

Harrows. There are many types of harrows: the zigzag type, which has staggered tines, is the commonest. Harrow tines are usually straight, but may vary in length and strength on the heavy and light types. *Drag harrows* have curved ends on the tines.

These implements are often used to complete the work of the cultivator. Besides breaking the soil down to a fine tilth they can have a useful consolidating effect due to shaking the soil about.

"Dutch" harrows have spikes fitted in a heavy wooden frame and are useful for levelling a seed-bed as well as breaking clods.

Some harrows, e.g. the chain type, consist of flexible links joined together to form a rectangle. These follow an uneven surface better, and do not jump about so much on grassland as the zigzag type. Most chain harrows have spikes fitted on one side. They are sometimes used to roll-up weeds such as "couch" grass.

Special types of harrows fitted with knife-like tines are used for improving matted grassland, by tearing out surface trash.

Hoes. These are implements used for controlling weeds between the rows in root crops. Various shaped blades, and discs may be fitted to them. Most types are either front, mid or rear mounted on a tractor. The front and mid mounted types are controlled by the steering of the tractor driver. The rear mounted types usually require a second person for steering the hoe.

Disc harrows consist of "gangs" of saucer-shaped discs about 12–24 in. in diameter. They have a cutting and consolidating effect on the soil and this is particularly useful when working a seed-bed on ploughed-out grassland.

The more the discs are *angled*, the greater will be:

(a) the depth of penetration,
(b) the cutting and breaking effect on the clods,
(c) the draught.

To increase the effect of the operation, the rear gangs should be angled more than the front gangs. Disc harrows are widely used for preparing all kinds of seed-beds but it should be remembered that they are expensive implements to use. They have a heavy draught and lots of wearing parts (discs, bearings and linkages) so should only be used when harrows would not be suitable. They tend to cut up the rhizomes of weeds such as "couch" and creeping thistle and this often encourages the spread of these weeds. Discing of old grassland before ploughing will usually allow the plough to do better work and a better seed-bed can be made. Heavy discs, and especially those with scalloped edges, are very useful for working in chopped straw after combining.

Rotary cultivators (e.g. rotavator). This type of implement consists of curved blades which rotate round a horizontal shaft set at right angles to the direction of travel. The shaft is driven from the P.T.O. of the tractor; depth is controlled by a land wheel or skid. This implement can produce a good tilth in difficult conditions and in many cases may replace all other implements in seed-bed preparation. A light fluffy tilth is sometimes produced which may "cap" easily if wet weather follows. The fineness of tilth can be controlled by the forward speed of the tractor—fast speed, coarse tilth. It is a very useful implement for mixing into the soil the remains of kale and sprout crops, or straw. The rotating action of the blades helps to drive the implement forward; so extra care must be taken when going down steep slopes. The blades cut up rhizomatous weeds (e.g. couch) but if the implement is used several times (at 10–14 day intervals) in growing weather it can completely destroy the couch either by burying the sprouted pieces or throwing them out on the surface to die off in drying winds. A similar method (working 8–10 in. deep) will control bracken.

In wet heavy soils the rotating action of the blades may have a smearing effect on the soil. This can usually be avoided by having the blades properly angled. "Rotavating" of ploughed or cultivated land when the surface is frozen in winter can produce a good seed-bed for cereals in the spring without any further working or loss of moisture; if there is couch present and the weather is dry, much of it may die off. Narrow rotary cultivator units are available for working between rows of root crops.

A recently introduced high-speed rotary cultivator is useful for quick shallow working either for stubble cleaning or seed-bed preparation.

Rolls. These are used to consolidate the top few inches of the soil so that plant roots can keep in contact with the soil particles and the soil can hold more moisture. They are also used for crushing clods and breaking surface crusts (caps). Rolls should not be used when the soil is wet—this is especially important on the heavier soils. The two main types of rolls are the *flat* roll which has a smooth surface and the *Cambridge* or *ring* roll which has a ribbed surface and consists of a number of heavy iron wheels or rings (about 3 in. wide) each of which has a ridge about $1\frac{1}{2}$ in. high. The rings are free to move independently and this helps to keep the surface clean. The ribbed or corrugated surface left by the Cambridge roll provides an excellent seed-bed on which to sow grass and clover seeds or roots. Also, it is less likely to "cap" than a flat rolled surface.

When rolling a growing crop, e.g. young cereals, tractor wheel-slip must be avoided as this will tear out the seedlings.

Very heavy rolls are sometimes used for levelling fields in the spring prior to taking a white clover seed crop.

A furrow press is a special type of very heavy ring roller (usually with three or four wheels) used for compressing the furrow slices after ploughing—it is usually attached to and pulled alongside the plough.

See simplified cultivation, Table 5, p. 85.

PANS

A *pan* is a hard, cement-like layer in the soil or subsoil which can be very harmful because it prevents surplus water draining away freely and restricts root growth.

Such a layer may be caused by ploughing at the same depth every year. This is a *plough pan* and is partly caused by the base of the plough sliding along the furrow. It is more likely to occur if rubber-tyred tractors are used when the soil is wet and there is some wheel-slip which has a smearing effect on the bottom of the furrow. Plough pans are more likely to form on the heavier types of soil. They can be broken up by using a *subsoiler*—a strong tine which can penetrate deeper than the plough, or, if the pan is not too deep, it can be destroyed by deep ploughing.

Pans may also be formed by the deposition of *iron compounds*, and sometimes *humus*, in layers in the soil or subsoil. These are often called *chemical* or *iron pans* and may be destroyed in the same way as plough pans. *Clay pans* are sometimes formed in certain soil formation processes.

SOIL CAPPING

A soil *cap* is a hard crust, often only about an inch thick, which sometimes forms on the surface of a soil.

It is most likely to form on soils which are low in organic matter. Heavy rain or large droplets of water from rain guns (see "Irrigation") may cause soil capping. Tractor wheels (especially if slipping), trailers and other heavy machinery can also cause capping in wet weather.

Although a soil cap is easily destroyed by weathering (e.g. frost, or wetting and drying) or by cultivations, it may do harm while it lasts by:

(a) preventing water moving into the soil,
(b) preventing air moving into and out of the soil in wet weather,
(c) hindering the development of seedlings from small seeds such as grasses and clovers, roots and vegetables.

CONTROL OF WEEDS BY CULTIVATION

The introduction of chemicals which kill weeds has reduced the importance of cultivations as a means of controlling weeds. The cereal crops are now regarded by many farmers as the *cleaning crops* instead of the roots and potato crops, mainly because chemical spraying of weeds in cereals is very effective.

However, weeds should be tackled in every way possible and there are still occasions when it is worthwhile to use cultivation methods.

Annual weeds can be tackled by:

(a) Working the stubble after harvest (e.g. discing, cultivating or rotavating) to encourage seeds to germinate: these young weeds can later be destroyed by harrowing or ploughing.

D

(b) Preparing a "false" seed-bed in spring to allow the weed seeds to germinate—these can be killed by cultivations before sowing root crops.

(c) Inter-row hoeing of root crops which can destroy a lot of annual weeds and some perennials.

Perennial weeds, e.g. couch grass, creeping thistle, docks, field bindweed and coltsfoot, can only be satisfactorily controlled by fallowing (i.e. cultivating the soil periodically through the growing season instead of cropping) but this is expensive. A fair amount of control can be obtained by short term working in dry weather.

Couch grass is easily killed by drying winds if the rhizomes can be dragged out to the surface free of soil. This may be done in August and September, or in the early spring, using cultivators or shallow ploughing to loosen the soil, followed by drag or spring tined harrows to drag it out on top and shake off the soil; dry weather is necessary to do this properly,

In damp soil conditions, the rotary cultivator can be used three or four times at fortnightly intervals to chop up and exhaust couch grass rhizomes. It is very important that the first time over should be on firm soil (e.g. stubble), and the tractor moving in low gear. Chopping the rhizomes into short pieces encourages nearly all the buds to send out shoots and so helps to exhaust them.

The deeper rooted bindweed, docks, thistle and coltsfoot cannot be satisfactorily controlled by these methods, but periodic hoeing and cultivating between the rows of root crops can considerably reduce these weeds by cutting off new shoots and so exhausting them.

Fallowing

The object of a long term fallow is to dry out the soil by frequent working and so dry out and kill the perennial weeds. On the medium to lighter soils this is done by frequent cultivations. On heavy soil, the field is ploughed when damp in spring to make it dry into hard lumps. These lumps are then moved by cross-ploughing or deep cultivations to help dry them out. During the summer, alternate

TABLE 5. A SIMPLIFIED CULTIVATIONS TABLE (A ROTARY CULTIVATOR OR OTHER POWER DRIVEN MACHINE MAY BE USED INSTEAD OF SOME OF THE OPERATIONS GIVEN BELOW)

		Autumn	Spring
Winter cereals	After grass	Plough, disc and/or harrow, drill, harrow.	Harrow and/or roll (if necessary).
	After potatoes	Cultivate or disc, drill, harrow.	
Spring cereals	After grass	Plough.	Harrow and/or disc, drill, harrow, roll.
	After cereals	Plough *or* disc and cultivate several times and leave in ridges over winter	Harrow and/or disc, drill, harrow, roll.
Roots, e.g. sugar-beet, swedes	After cereals	Stubble cleaning, plough-in F.Y.M.	Disc and/or harrow, roll, drill; inter-row hoeing.
Kale			In the wetter areas, the field is ridged up before drilling.
Potatoes	After cereals	Stubble cleaning, plough-in F.Y.M.	Cross-plough, if necessary. Cultivate (twice), harrow, ridge, plant and split ridges followed by inter-row cultivations and finally earthing-up.
	After grass	Rotavate or disc, plough.	Cultivations after planting may be replaced by chemical weed control.
Peas		Plough, fast and well.	Harrow, drill.

periods of wetting and drying break the lumps down to a fine tilth and then annual weeds may germinate to be destroyed by further working. Fallowing is not very common nowadays because of the cost of the work and the loss of profit on a crop.

One of the best methods of controlling wild onion is by taking seven spring sown crops in succession and ploughing each year in November.

Thorough cultivations which provide the most suitable conditions for rapid healthy growth of the crop may result in the crop outgrowing and smothering the weeds.

Suggestions for Classwork

Examine:

(a) Samples of rock, e.g. granite, basalt, chalk, limestone.
(b) Various soil types in the field or in suitable blocks in the classroom, e.g. clay, sand, loam, peat. Handle them when wet and dry. If possible, examine the soil profiles.
(c) Note the crumbling effect on clods of frost action, and wetting and drying.
(d) Visit farms on clay, loam and sandy soils and discuss the management of these soils.
(e) Visit a drainage scheme in progress. Note how levels are taken and the use of sighting and boning rods.
(f) See seed-beds being prepared for cereals, roots and potatoes and make notes on the cultivation work which was carried out.

CHAPTER 3

FERTILIZERS AND MANURES

Supplying Plant Nutrients to the Soil

If good crops are to be continuously removed from a field or a farm then there must be at least as many nutrients returned to the soil as have been removed in the crops. Table 6 gives average figures for nutrients removed by various crops.

When supplying nutrients to the soil it is usual to apply more than enough for the needs of each crop because some nutrients may be lost by drainage (e.g. nitrogen and potash) and some will become "fixed" or unavailable in the soil (e.g. phosphate). Where one crop, e.g. potatoes or roots, has been heavily manured with fertilizers and F.Y.M., it may be possible to reduce the amount of nutrients supplied to the following crop.

Nitrogen is supplied by fertilizers, organic matter (e.g. F.Y.M.), nodule bacteria on legumes (e.g. clovers, peas, beans, lucerne), and nitrogen fixing micro-organisms in the soil. It is difficult to estimate how much nitrogen is produced by legumes and micro-organisms; clovers in grassland may supply 100–200 units per acre, and micro-organisms about 50 units per acre per annum.

Phosphates and *potash* are supplied by the soil minerals, organic manures and fertilizers.

The farmer has to decide each year what fertilizers to put on each crop. This is partly a haphazard choice and partly based on the results of experiments and his previous experience on his farm. Soil analysis, as at present carried out, gives no indication of nitrogen requirements, and is only a very rough guide to the need for phosphates and potash.

TABLE 6. NUTRIENTS REMOVED BY CROPS (IN LB)

Crop (good average yield/acre)	N	P_2O_5	K_2O	
Wheat				
40 cwt grain	83	38	27	
40 cwt straw	15	6	36	If cereal straw is burnt on the field after combining, the potash is not lost but may be unevenly distributed.
Total	98	44	63	
Barley				
33 cwt grain	60	30	20	
25 cwt straw	15	4	28	
Total	75	34	48	
Oats				
26 cwt grain	50	24	16	
30 cwt straw	10	6	50	
Total	60	30	66	
Potatoes				
12 tons tubers	90	40	160	The response to phosphatic fertilizers is greater than these figures suggest.
1 ton dry haulm	45	5	100	
Total	135	45	260	
Sugar-beet				
16 tons washed roots	64	35	70	If the sugar-beet tops or kale are eaten by stock on the field where grown then most of the nutrients may be returned to the soil.
14 tons fresh tops	106	35	180	
Total	170	70	250	
Kale				
20 tons fresh crop	200	60	180	

TABLE 7. THE NEED FOR AND EFFECTS OF NITROGEN, PHOSPHORUS, AND POTASSIUM.

Plant nutrient	Crops which are most likely to suffer from deficiency	Field Conditions where deficiency is likely to occur	Deficiency symptoms	Effect on crop growth	Effects of excess	Time and method of application
Nitrogen (N)	All farm crops except legumes (e.g. beans, peas, clover). It is especially important for leafy crops such as grasses, cereals kales and cabbages.	On all soils, except peats, and especially where organic matter is low and after continuous cereal crops.	Thin, weak, spindly growth; lack of tillers and side shoots; small yellowish-green leaves, sometimes showing "autumn" tints.	Increases leaf size, rate of growth and yield. Produces darker green leaves.	Causes "lodging" of cereal crops. Delays ripening. Produces soft growth which is more susceptible to disease and frost. May spoil crop quality by lowering the starch or sugar content. If combine-drilled germination of seed may be damaged.	Nitrogen fertilizers applied in seed-bed or top-dressed in spring. Anhydrous ammonia may be injected about 6"–9" into the soil at up to 300 units/ac. to supply grass needs for a season.

TABLE 7. THE NEED FOR AND EFFECTS OF NITROGEN, PHOSPHORUS, AND POTASSIUM—continued

Plant nutrient	Crops which are most likely to suffer from deficiency	Field Conditions where deficiency is likely to occur	Deficiency symptoms	Effect on crop growth	Effects of excess	Time and method of application
Phosphorus (P)	Root crops (e.g. sugar-beet, mangolds, swedes, carrots), clovers, lucerne, potatoes and kale	Clay soils; acid soils —especially in high rainfall areas, chalk and limestone soils and peats. Poor grassland.	Similar to nitrogen except that leaves are a dull, bluish-green colour with purple or bronze tints.	Speeds up growth of seedlings and increases root development; hastens leaf growth and maturity. Encourages clover development in grassland. Improves quality of crops.	Might cause crops to ripen too early and so reduce yield if not balanced with nitrogen and potash fertilizers	Phosphorus fertilizers applied in seed-bed for arable crops; "placement" in bands near or with the seed reduces the amount which has to be applied. Broadcast on grassland in autumn or early spring.

Plant nutrient	Crops which are most likely to suffer from deficiency	Field Conditions where deficiency is likely to occur	Deficiency symptoms	Effect on crop growth	Effects of excess	Time and method of application
Potassium (K)	Potatoes, carrots, beans, barley, clovers, lucerne, sugar-beet and mangolds.	Light sandy soils, chalk soils, peats, badly drained soils, grassland which has been repeatedly cut for hay, silage or "zero" grazing.	Growth is squat, and growing points "die-back", e.g. edges and tip of leaves die and appear scorched.	Crops are healthy and resist disease and frost better. Prolongs growth. Improves quality of crops. Balances nitrogen and phosphate fertilizers.	May delay ripening too much. May cause magnesium deficiency in fruit and glasshouse crops and "grass-staggers" in grazing animals.	Potassium fertilizers applied in seed-bed for arable crops; "placement" in bands with or near the seed reduces the amount which has to be applied; care required if large amounts combine-drilled in dry seed-bed. Broadcast on grassland in autumn or late spring.

Table 7 sets out the main needs for nitrogen, phosphorus and potassium, and also the effects of deficiency and excess.

The quantities of nitrogen, phosphate and potash used are usually expressed as *units*; average recommendations are given in the chapters dealing with individual crops.

Units of Plant Food

A *unit* of plant food is 1% of 1 cwt (i.e. 1·12 lb).

A nitrogen fertilizer containing 21% N has 21 units of nitrogen in each cwt (112 lb). Similarly, a compound fertilizer containing 10% N, 12% P_2O_5 and 16% K_2O (usually given as 10:12:16) has 10 units of nitrogen, 12 units of phosphate and 16 units of potash in each cwt.

It is possible to compare the cost of fertilizers on a unit basis. For example:

Suppose 1 ton of sulphate of ammonia (21% N) costs £12 5s. 0d. net (total cost *less* subsidy),

then   1 cwt of sulphate of ammonia costs 12s. 3d.,

and so   1 unit of nitrogen in sulphate of ammonia costs $\dfrac{147d.}{21} = 7d.$

Also suppose 1 ton of "nitro-chalk" (21% N) costs £14 0s. 0d. net,

then   1 cwt of "nitro-chalk" costs 14s. 0d.,

and so   1 unit of nitrogen in "nitro-chalk" costs $\dfrac{168d.}{21} = 8d.$

Allowance must be made for the fact that part of the nitrogen in "nitro-chalk" is present in the slightly more available nitrate form and that "nitro-chalk" does not remove lime from the soil.

If   1 ton of muriate of potash (60% K_2O) costs £20,

then   1 cwt of muriate of potash costs 20s.,

and so 1 unit of K_2O costs $\dfrac{240d.}{60} = 4d.$ per unit.

Similarly, the cost of one unit of P_2O_5 is about 6d. per unit.

UNIT VALUES

These can be calculated as 1% of a cwt (see p. 92) or as 1% of a ton (as is usually done when calculating residual values—see p. 103).

Straight Fertilizers

Straight fertilizers supply only one of the major plant foods.

NITROGEN FERTILIZERS (N)

The nitrogen in many straight and compound fertilizers is in the ammonium (NH_4 ions) form but this is quickly changed by bacteria in the soil to the nitrate (NO_3 ions) form. Many crop plants, e.g. cereals, take up and respond to the NO_3 ions quicker than the NH_4 ions but other crops, e.g. grass and potatoes are equally responsive to NH_4 and NO_3 ions.

Commonly used nitrogen fertilizers are:

(1) *Sulphate of ammonia* (S/A), $(NH_4)_2SO_4$. This cheap and very important fertilizer consists of whitish needle-like crystals which contain about 21% of nitrogen. It is produced either as a by-product from gas-works or synthetically from the nitrogen in the atmosphere. It is soluble in water. The nitrogen is present in the ammonium (NH_4) form and is changed by bacteria in the soil to the nitrate (NO_3) form,—this happens quickly in warm soils. Every 1 cwt of sulphate of ammonia applied to the soil results in a loss of the equivalent of 1 cwt of limestone ($CaCO_3$). The sulphate part of the fertilizer combines with calcium (Ca) and is washed out of the soil.

(2) *The ammonium nitrate* group, NH_4NO_3 (35% N). Ammonium nitrate is a dangerous material by itself, especially if it is in a finely divided state, so it is mixed with limestone and sold under various trade names, e.g. "nitro-chalk"—21% N, and "nitra-shell"—23% N. These are slightly quicker acting than sulphate of ammonia on some crops because part of the nitrogen is in the readily available nitrate form. "Nitram" is ammonium nitrate in a prilled form (a safe type of granule); it contains 34·5% N.

(3) *Urea*. This is a very concentrated, water soluble fertilizer containing about 45% N. It is usually sold in a specially granulated form which stores and spreads satisfactorily. It is quickly changed to ammonium and nitrate forms by the soil bacteria.

(4) *Gas liquors*. These are dilute solutions (1–4% N) of ammonium compounds, containing some phenols and tarry substances, which are produced in the purification of coal gas. The commonly used one is the "10 oz liquor" (1·77% N) which contains 15 units of nitrogen per 100 gal. They are usually applied by the suppliers; the usual rate of application is 300 gal/acre. They are most effective when worked into the soil. Top-dressings are liable to cause some "scorch" and some loss of nitrogen into the atmosphere. They are sometimes used for weed control in kale and for spraying on straw before ploughing it in.

(5) *Anhydrous ammonia* (82% N) and *aqueous ammonia* (25-30% N) can be injected about 6″ into soil (to reduce loss of N) by a contract service.

PHOSPHATE FERTILIZERS (P)

By custom and by law the quality or grade of phosphate fertilizers is expressed as a percentage of phosphorus pentoxide (P_2O_5) equivalent.

(1) *Ground rock phosphate*. The natural rock ground to a fine powder—i.e. 90% should pass through a 100-mesh sieve (10,000 holes per square inch). The best ones contain about 29% P_2O_5 which is insoluble in water. They should only be used on acid soils in high rainfall areas and for grassland and brassica crops (e.g. swedes, turnips, kale).

(2) *Superphosphate* (super). This contains 18–21% water-soluble P_2O_5 produced by treating ground rock phosphate with sulphuric acid. It also contains gypsum ($CaSO_4$), which may remain as a white residue in the soil, and a small amount of unchanged rock phosphate. It is suitable for all crops and all soil conditions.

(3) *Triple superphosphate.* This contains about 47% water-soluble P_2O_5 and is produced by treating the rock phosphate with phosphoric acid. 1 cwt triple super = $2\frac{1}{2}$ cwt ordinary super.

(4) *Basic slags.* These are by-products in the manufacture of steel. The total amount of phosphate present varies between about 8–22% P_2O_5. This is insoluble in water but most of it may be soluble in a 2% citric acid solution (this is a guide to its solubility in the soil). A good slag should have a high percentage P_2O_5; a high proportion of this (80% +) should be *citric soluble* and over 80% should pass through a 100-mesh sieve. Slags are not so quick acting as "supers" and give best results on acid soils. Cattle may be poisoned by eating herbage recently treated with slag which has not been washed off the leaves. Rate of application 6–10 cwt/acre. Slags contain some trace elements.

POTASH FERTILIZERS (K)

The quality or grade of potash fertilizers is expressed as a percentage of potassium oxide (K_2O) equivalent.

(1) *Muriate of potash* M/P (potassium chloride) as now sold usually contains 60% K_2O. It does not store very well and does not spread easily unless specially treated. This is the commonest source of potash for farm use and for the manufacture of compounds containing potash.

(2) *Sulphate of potash* S/P (potassium sulphate). This is made from the muriate and so is more expensive per unit K_2O. It contains 48–50% K_2O and is the best type to use for quality production of crops such as potatoes, tomatoes and other market garden crops.

(3) *Kainit and potash salts.* These are usually a mixture of potassium and sodium salts, and sometimes magnesium salts. They contain about 12–30% K_2O. They have most value for sugar-beet and similar crops for which the sodium is a useful plant food.

SALT

Common salt (sodium chloride) is a cheap and useful fertilizer for sugar-beet and similar crops—applied at the rate of 3–5 cwt/acre.

Compound or Mixed Fertilizers

These fertilizers supply *two* or *three* of the major plant foods. (i.e. nitrogen, phosphorus and potassium). They are produced by mixing such fertilizers as sulphate of ammonia, superphosphate and muriate of potash or by more complex chemical processes.

About 75% of all fertilizers now used in this country are compounds. These are *well mixed* by machinery, are *granulated* and *store well*. This is a great saving in labour at a busy time because fertilizers mixed on the farm do not store well.

The concentration of compounds varies widely; some recently introduced contain over 50 units of plant food per cwt, e.g. 15% N, 15% P_2O_5, 23% K_2O. If fertilizers are mixed on the farm it is possible to calculate the analysis of the mixture as follows:

Suppose the following are mixed:

    2 parts sulphate of ammonia,
    3 parts superphosphate and
    1 part muriate of potash.

	N	P	K
200 lb of S/A (21%) contain	42 lb	—	—
300 lb of super (18%) contain	—	54 lb	—
100 lb of M/P (60%) contain	—	—	60 lb
600 lb of the mixture contain	42 lb	54 lb	60 lb
100 lb of the mixture contain	7 lb	9 lb	10 lb

The analysis of the mixture is therefore 7:9:10.

Purchased compound fertilizers usually cost about £2 0s. 0d. more per ton than the equivalent in "straights".

Plant Food Ratios

Fertilizers containing different amounts of plant food may have the same plant food ratios. For example:

Fertilizer	Ratio	Equivalent rates of application
(a) 12:12:18	1:1:1½	5 cwt of (a) = 4 cwt of (b)
(b) 15:15:23	1:1:1½	
(c) 15:10:10	1½:1:1	7 cwt of (c) = 5 cwt of (d)
(d) 21:14:14	1½:1:1	

Some examples of compounds and possible uses:

Compound (N:P:K)	Crop	Rate/acre (cwt)	Units/acre (N	P	K)
10:10:18	potatoes	10	100	100	180
20:10:10	spring cereal	4	80	40	40
0:20:20	autumn cereal	2	0	40	40
10:20:20	autumn cereal	2	20	40	40

Fertilizers are supplied in various ways:

Solids

(a) 1 cwt *paper bags* (usually five ply).

(b) 1 cwt *plastic bags*—can be stored outside.

(c) *Bulk.*—can be stored in dry, concrete bays covered with plastic sheets. 1 ton occupies about 35 ft³. It can be removed by tractor hydraulic loaders or augers into trailers or trailer spreaders. It is also possible to have it supplied to the field in self unloading bins each holding about 2 tons.

Liquids. This is a fairly new method. The liquid compounds are, as yet, not so concentrated as the solids; usually 9 gal of liquids are equivalent to about 1 cwt of solid fertilizer. The liquids can be sprayed on the soil or crop or injected into the soil with special tines. Some examples of analysis: 9:9:9; 7:6:12.

Liquid fertilizers can be applied very accurately.

Application of Fertilizers

The main methods used are:

(a) *Broadcast distributors* using various mechanisms such as:

    (1) *"Plate and flicker" type.* Revolving saucer-shaped discs at the bottom of the hopper carry fertilizer to the front or the rear of the box where it is flicked off by swiftly revolving fingers. This is one of the most accurate types of distributor.

    (2) Other types involving rollers, brushes, chains, etc.

    (3) *Spinning disc* types. These may be mounted or semi-mounted on the three-point tractor linkage or may be trailer types. Accuracy of distribution varies considerably, and is very dependent on accurate setting and amount of overlap.

(b) *Combine drills.* Fertilizer and seed (e.g. cereals) from separate hoppers is fed down the same or an adjoining spout. A *star-wheel* feed mechanism is normally used for the fertilizer and this usually produces a "dollop" effect along the rows. In soils low in phosphate and potash this method of *placement* of the fertilizer is much more efficient than broadcasting.

(c) *Placement drills.* These machines usually place the fertilizer in bands 2–3 in. to the side and 1–2 in. below the rows of seeds. It is more efficient than broadcasting for crops such as peas, and also sugar-beet on some soils, e.g. sandy soils. Other types of placement drills attached to the planter are used for applying fertilizers to the potato crop.

(d) *Broadcast from aircraft.* This is useful for top-dressing of cereals—especially in a wet spring; also for applying fertilizers in inaccessible areas such as hill grazings. Highly concentrated fertilizers should be used, e.g. urea.

(e) Liquids injected under pressure into the soil.

MACHINERY MAINTENANCE

All machinery for fertilizer application should be thoroughly washed after use and coated with a rust-proofing material during long idle periods.

Organic Manures

FARMYARD MANURE (F.Y.M.)

This consists of dung and urine, and the litter used for bedding stock. It is not a standardized product, and its value depends on:

(1) *The kind of animal that makes it.* If animals are fed strictly according to maintenance and production requirements, the quality of dung produced by various classes of stock will be similar. But in practice it is generally found that as cows and young stock utilize much of the nitrogen and phosphate in their food, their dung is poorer than that produced by fattening stock.

(2) *The kind of food fed to the animal that makes the dung.* The richer the food in minerals, the richer will be the dung. But it is uneconomical to feed a rich diet just to produce a richer dung.

(3) *The amount of straw used.* The less straw used, the more concentrated will be the manure and the more rapidly will it break down to a "short" friable condition.

Straw is the best type of litter available, although bracken, peat moss, sawdust and wood shavings can be used. About 30 cwt of straw per animal is needed in a covered yard for 6 months, and between 40–60 cwt in a semi-covered or open yard.

(4) *The manner of storage.* There can be considerable losses from F.Y.M. because of bad storage.

Dung from cowsheds, cubicles and milking parlours should, if possible, be put into a heap which is protected from the elements to prevent the washing out and dilution of a large percentage of the plant foods which it contains. Dung made in yards should preferably remain there until it is spread on the land, and then, to prevent further loss, it is advisable to plough it in immediately.

F.Y.M. is important chiefly because of the valuable physical effects on the soil of the humus it contains. It is also a very valuable source of plant foods, particularly nitrogen, phosphate and potash, as well as other elements in smaller amounts. Ten tons of well made F.Y.M. contain approximately 100 units N, 60 units P_2O_5 and 100 units K_2O. Much of the nitrogen may be lost before it is ploughed in and all the plant food in F.Y.M. is less available compared with that in chemical fertilizers.

Application. The application of F.Y.M. will be dealt with under the various crops.

LIQUID MANURE, SLURRY AND EFFLUENT

Liquid manure is a valuable material, being particularly rich in nitrogen and potash. But the problems of its collection and conservation tend to outweigh its usefulness. From yards, the most practical method of dealing with liquid manure is simply to supply enough straw to absorb all the liquid, and thus a good sample of dung will be produced. But apart from this, more often than not, these days, the liquid manure is allowed to run away with water wash as slurry.

In recent years, the need to economize in the use of bedding straw has led to larger areas of concrete in and around stock buildings and also slatted floors and the cubicle system of housing cattle. Slurry is the term commonly used for the mixture of dung, urine, washing water and rainwater which is produced from such places. Effluent is another term used but is also includes other liquids such as that from silage.

Slurry or effluent must not be allowed to flow into and pollute rivers (or ditches leading to rivers) and so it must be returned to the land. It has some manurial value which varies considerably and depends mainly on the amount of water present. On average, 1000 gal of slurry contain about 25 units N, 20 units P_2O_5 and 25 units K_2O (see M.A.F.F. leaflet, STL No. 44).

Several methods are used in dealing with slurry. For example, it can be pushed into a large tank and then pumped out through a special irrigation system or taken out with a trailer sludge tank and spread on the fields. About $1-1\frac{1}{2}$ ft³ of storage will be required per cow per day for dung and urine alone. On light, free-draining land, one of the simplest methods of disposal is to push it up and over a ramp into a heap. This heap may be enclosed by a wall of bales and netting wire, or railway sleepers. Most of the liquid soaks away or evaporates and during the summer it is usually dry enough to be lifted with a fore-end loader and then spread on the land. Soak-away ditches and pits can also be used, but they may require to be cleaned out occasionally.

CEREAL STRAWS

Straw is a valuable source of organic matter, although its plant food content is low. By ploughing-in straw on poor, light soils, the soil structure is improved. On these poor soils, it is advisable to apply 20 units N for every ton of straw (which is produced from approximately 1 acre) ploughed in to supply the needs of the bacteria which rot down the straw. On fertile soils the nitrogen is unnecessary.

But there are practical difficulties in the ploughing-in of straw. It must be spread evenly; ideally it should be chopped, and good ploughing is necessary to bury it. Because of all this, unwanted straw is often burnt unless it can be sold at a reasonable price.

THE LEY

The ley is a good producer of organic matter. It forms the basis of the alternate husbandry system of farming, whereby fertility and soil structure are built up when the field is in grass, and this in-creased fertility can be utilized by a succession of arable crops before the field is put back to grass.

GREEN MANURING

This is the practice of growing and ploughing in green crops to increase the organic matter content of the soil. It is normally only carried out on light soils.

White mustard is the most commonly grown crop. Sown at 8–15 lb/acre it can produce a crop ready for ploughing within 6–8 weeks. It can also provide useful cover for pheasants. Leguminous crops such as vetches are also sometimes grown.

But green manuring does not appreciably increase the organic matter in the soil. It is a rather unsatisfactory substitute for F.Y.M., straw and the ley.

SEAWEED

Seaweed is often used instead of F.Y.M. for crops such as early potatoes in coastal areas, e.g. Ayrshire, Cornwall and the Channel Islands. Ten tons contain about 100 units of N, 20 units P_2O_5 and 270 units K_2O. It also contains about 350 lb of salt. The organic matter in seaweed breaks down rapidly.

POULTRY MANURE

The composition varies according to where it has been produced and stored. When partly dried it can be handled as F.Y.M., or, it may be treated as slurry after mixing with water.

Source	Average units per ton		
	N	P_2O_5	K_2O
Fresh manure, e.g. from battery cages	40	40	15
Air-dried manure	70	70	30
Straw yards	12	8	12
Deep litter	40	50	30

Poultry manure is relatively deficient in potash.

WASTE ORGANIC MATERIALS

Various waste products are used for market garden crops—partly as a source of organic matter and partly because they release nitrogen slowly to the crop. They are usually too expensive for ordinary farm crops.

Shoddy (waste wool and cotton) contains 100–300 units of nitrogen per ton. Waste wool is best, and is applied at 1–2 tons/acre.

Dried blood, ground *hoof and horn* and *meat and bone meal* are also used; the nitrogen composition is variable.

Residual Values of Fertilizers and Manures

The nutrients in most manures and fertilizers are not used up completely in the year of application. The amount likely to remain for use in the following years is taken into account when compensating outgoing farm tenants.

All the *nitrogen* in *soluble* nitrogen fertilizers (e.g. sulphate of ammonia, nitro-chalk, compounds, and in dried blood) is used in the first year.

For *nitrogen* in bones, hoof and horn, meat and bone meal: Allow $\frac{1}{2}$ after one crop and $\frac{1}{4}$ after two crops.

Phosphate in *soluble* form, e.g. super, basic slag, compounds: Allow $\frac{2}{3}$ after one crop, $\frac{1}{3}$ after two and $\frac{1}{6}$ after three crops.

Phosphate in *insoluble* form, e.g. bones, ground rock phosphate: Allow $\frac{1}{3}$ after one crop, $\frac{1}{6}$ after two and $\frac{1}{12}$ after three.

Potash, e.g. muriate or sulphate of potash, compounds: Allow $\frac{1}{2}$ after one crop and $\frac{1}{4}$ after two.

Lime: one-eighth of the cost is subtracted each year after application.

Suggestions for Classwork

(1) Examine samples of all the commonly used "straight" fertilizers and a few compounds and note differences between them.

(2) Visit experimental farms or demonstration plots to see the differences in crop growth due to deficient, excess and correct supply of nutrients.

(3) If possible, visit farms to see bulk and sack storage of fertilizers, methods of handling and application.

(4) When visiting farms note the various methods used for handling F.Y.M. and slurry.

CHAPTER 4

CROPPING

Climate and Weather and their Effects on Cropping

Climate has an important influence on the type of crops which can be grown satisfactorily nearly every year. It may be defined as a seasonal average of the many *weather* conditions.

Weather is the state of the atmosphere at any time—it is the combined effect of such conditions as heat or cold, wetness or dryness, wind or calm, clearness or cloudiness, pressure and the electric state of the air.

The daily, monthly and yearly changes of temperature and rainfall give a fairly good indication of the conditions likely to be found.

Average yearly figures such as 40 in. rainfall and temperature 50°F are of very limited value.

The climate of this country is mainly influenced by:

(1) its distance from the equator (50–60°N latitude.)
(2) the warm Gulf Stream which flows along the western coasts.
(3) the prevailing south-west winds.
(4) the numerous "lows" or "depressions" which cross from west to east and bring most of the rainfall.
(5) the distribution of highland and lowland—most of the hilly and mountainous areas are on the west side.
(6) its nearness to the continent of Europe; from there hot winds in summer and very cold winds in winter can affect the weather in the southern and eastern areas.

Local variations are caused by *altitude, aspect* and *slope*.

Altitude (height above sea level) can affect climate in many ways. The temperature drops about 1°F for every 300 ft rise above sea level. Every 50 ft rise in height usually shortens the growing season by 2 days (one in spring and one in autumn) and it may check the rate of growth during the year. High land is more likely to be buffeted by strong winds and is likely to receive more rain from the moisture-laden prevailing winds which are cooled as they rise upwards.

Aspect (the direction in which land faces) can affect the amount of sunshine (heat) absorbed by the soil. In this country the temperature of north-facing slopes may be 2°F (1°C) lower than on similar slopes facing south.

Slope. When air cools down it becomes heavier and will move down a slope and force warmer air upwards. This is why frost often occurs on the lowest ground on clear still nights whereas the upper slopes may remain free of frost. "Frost pockets" occur where cold air collects in hollows or alongside obstructing banks, walls, hedges, etc. (see Fig. 35). Frost-susceptible crops such as early potatoes, maize and fruit should not be grown in such places.

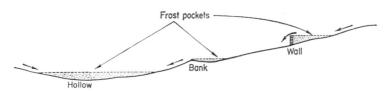

Fig. 35. Diagram to show how frost pockets are formed as cold air flows down a slope.

RAINFALL IN THE BRITISH ISLES

This comes mainly from the moist south-westerly winds and from the many "lows" or "depressions" which cross from west to east.

Western areas receive much more rain than eastern areas—partly because of the west to east movement of the rain-bearing air and partly because most of the highland is along the western side of the country.

The average annual rainfall on lowland areas in the west is about 35 in. and in the east is about 25 in. It is much greater on higher land.

TEMPERATURE OF THE BRITISH ISLES

The temperature changes are mainly due to:

(1) the seasonal changes in length of day and intensity of sunlight,
(2) the source of the wind, e.g. whether it is a mild south-westerly, or whether it is cold polar air from the north or from the continent in winter.
(3) local variations in altitude and aspect.
(4) night temperatures are usually higher when there is cloud cover which prevents too much heat escaping into the upper atmosphere.

The soil temperature may also be affected by colour—dark soils absorb more heat than light-coloured soils. Also, damp soils can absorb more heat than dry soils.

The average January temperature in lowland areas along the west side of the country is about 42°F (6°C) and about 39°F (4°C) along the east side.

The average July temperatures in lowland areas in the southern counties is about 62°F (17°C) but this drops to about 55°F (13°C) in the north of Scotland.

CROPPING IN THE BRITISH ISLES

Grass grows well in the wetter, western areas and so dairying, stock rearing and fattening can be successfully carried on in these areas.

The drier areas in the east are best suited to arable crops which require fairly dry weather for easy harvesting.

The mild, frost-free areas in the south-west of England and Wales (i.e. parts of Devon, Cornwall, and Pembroke) are suitable for early crops of potatoes, broccoli, flowers, etc. The Isle of Thanet (Kent) and the Ayrshire coast are also early areas free from late frosts.

The more exposed hill and mountain areas are unsuitable for intensive production because of the lower temperatures, very high rainfall, inaccessibility and steep slopes. These are mainly rough grazings used for extensive cattle and sheep rearing. Large areas are now forestry plantations.

Most of the chalk and oolitic limestone areas (in the south and east) are now used for large scale cereal production—particularly barley. The leys grown in these areas are mainly used by dairy cattle or sheep, or for herbage seed production. Cereals are grown on all types of soil. Maincrop potatoes and root crops, such as sugar-beet, are grown on the deeper loamy soils of the midlands and eastern counties. Carrots are grown on some light soils in the eastern counties.

Mixed farming (i.e. both crop and stock enterprises on the same farm) is found on most lowland farms. The proportion of grass (and so stock) to arable crops usually varies according to soil type and rainfall. The heavier soils and high rainfall areas usually have more grass than arable crops.

Rotations

A *rotation* is a cropping system in which two or more crops are grown in a fixed sequence. If the rotation includes a period in grass, (a ley), which is used for grazing and conservation, the system is sometimes called "alternate husbandry" or mixed farming. The term "ley farming" describes a system where a farm or group of fields is cropped entirely with leys which are re-seeded at regular intervals; some people describe any cropping system which includes leys as "ley farming".

Farm crops may be grouped as follows:

(a) *Cereals* (*wheat, barley, oats* and *rye*). These are *exhaustive* crops because they are removed from the field and usually sold off the farm (i.e. they are cash crops). They encourage weeds—especially grass weeds such as couch. If grown continuously on the same field, fungus diseases such as take-all and eyespot, or pests such as eelworms can seriously reduce yields. Continuous spring barley crops are least likely to suffer losses. Cereals have peak demands for labour in autumn (ploughing and some sowing), spring (sowing) and late summer (harvesting). Large-scale mechanization has greatly simplified cereal production.

(b) *Potatoes* and *root crops* such as *sugar-beet, mangolds, carrots,* etc. These are mainly high value cash crops and require deep soils. They have heavy demands for plant nutrients but allow the farmer to use large amounts of fertilizers and F.Y.M. and so build up fertility. Timely cultivations before sowing and during the early growth period can control most troublesome weeds—hence the reason for regarding this group as "cleaning" crops. This is expensive and chemical weed control is being introduced. It is very risky to grow any of these crops continuously—mainly because of eelworms. This group has a high labour demand—especially for harvesting of potatoes and singling of sugar-beet. However, mechanization has solved many of the problems.

(c) *Pulse crops* e.g. *peas* and *beans.* In many ways these crops resemble cereals but they can build up nitrogen in the nodules on their roots. They should not be grown continuously because of build-up of fungus diseases (e.g. clover and bean rot) and pests (e.g. pea root eelworm). They can provide a break from continuous cereal growing.

(d) *Restorative crops,* i.e. the crops which are usually fed off on the fields and so return nutrients and organic matter to the soil.

The best examples, are *leys, kale* and *roots for folding off.*

A good crop rotation would include several crops because this would:

(1) reduce the financial risk if one crop yielded or sold badly,
(2) spread the labour requirements more evenly over the year,
(3) reduce the risk of diseases and pests associated with single cropping (mono-culture),
(4) probably give better control of weeds,
(5) provide more interest for the farmer.

However, most of these objectives could be obtained without having a rigid system of cropping. The present tendency is to break away from traditional systems and to simplify the cropping programme as much as possible.

This approach has been encouraged by:

(1) the need to economize in labour and capital expenditure,
(2) better machinery for growing and harvesting crops,
(3) much better control of pests and diseases—mainly by chemicals and resistant varieties,
(4) chemical weed control,
(5) guaranteed price systems for most crops.

Many well tried rotations have been practised in various parts of the country. One of the earliest and best known was the *Norfolk Four-Course* rotation which was well suited to arable areas in Eastern England.

It started as:

Turnips or *swedes*	Folded off with sheep in winter.	Roots
Spring barley (undersown)	Cash crop.	Cereal
Red clover	Grazed in spring and summer.	Ley
Winter wheat	Cash crop.	Cereal

This was a well balanced rotation for:

(1) building up and maintenance of soil fertility,
(2) control of weeds and pests,
(3) employment of labour throughout the year,
(4) providing a reasonable profit.

However, considerable changes have occurred over the years mainly due to:

(1) the introduction of fertilizers, other crops and better machinery,
(2) greater freedom of cropping for tenant farmers,
(3) the need for increased profits.

Some of the *changes* which have occurred are:

(1) *Sugar-beet*, *potatoes*, *mangolds*, and *carrots* have replaced all or part of the folded roots.

(2) *Beans* and *peas* have replaced red clover in some areas or alternatively a two- or three-year *ley* has been introduced.

(3) Two or three successive cereal crops have replaced the barley and wheat crops.

An example of a wide variation is:

Winter wheat	⎫
1 or 2 crops of spring barley	⎬ Replacing winter wheat.
Sugar-beet or potatoes	Root break.
1–3 cereal crops	Replacing spring barley.
2–4-year ley	Replacing 1-year red clover ley.

Where there is a big difference in the types of soil on a farm it may be advisable to have one rotation for the heavy soils and another for the light soils.

The most suitable rotation or cropping programme for a farm must be based on the management plan for the farm. It should provide grazing and other foods for the livestock and also the maximum possible acreage of cash crops. The cash crops grown will partly depend on the amount of labour available throughout the year.

Catch Cropping

This is the practice of taking a quick growing crop between two major crops. With the dairy herd and sheep flock it can be very profitable provided:

(1) It does not interfere with the following main crop. This can happen when the main crop is planted late in a badly prepared seed-bed.

(2) The catch crop is not grown when more attention should have been given to cleaning the land of weeds.

(3) It is grown cheaply, without expensive seed-bed preparation, and with limited use of fertilizers, except possibly nitrogen.

Examples of catch cropping

(1) Main crop   Cereal
    Catch crop   Italian ryegrass at 20–30 lb/acre (or I.R.G. with
                 yellow trefoil).
                 This grass can provide:
                   (a) stubble grazing,
                   (b) early bite (see Table 15),
                   (c) possibly another grazing, or silage cut before
                       planting,
    Main crop   Kale.

(2) Main crop   2nd early potatoes (harvested in July) or a ley
                 (ploughed in July).
    Catch crop   Rye and ryegrass to provide:
                   (a) possibly an autumn graze (depending upon
                       the season),
                   (b) early bite,
                   (c) silage before planting,
    Main crop   Kale.

(3) Main crop   Winter wheat, undersown in autumn with
    Catch crop   3–4 lb Italian ryegrass.
                 This will produce and shed seed before harvest
                 and this usually provides:
                   (a) early bite,
                   (b) possibly another grazing, or silage cut before
                       planting,
    Main crop   Roots or kale.

Cereals

The *cereal* (*corn,* or *grain*) crops grown in this country are *wheat,*
barley, oats, rye and *maize.* Wheat and barley are the most important.

The introduction of combine-drills, combine-harvesters, driers,
and bulk handling has greatly simplified and improved cereal

production. Weeds can be controlled fairly easily by selective chemicals—see chapter on "Weed Control".

These crops are easily recognized by their well known *ears* (flowering heads). They can be recognized in the early, leafy stages as shown in Fig. 36.

Although it is common practice now to use *weight* measures (hundredweights) for seed rates and yields of cereals, *volume* measures (e.g. bushel and sack) are still used in some areas. The following table gives a comparison for average quality grain.

TABLE 8.

	Wheat	Barley	Oats	Rye
Peck (2 gal)	16 lb	14 lb	10½ lb	14 lb
Bushel (4 pecks)	64 lb	56 lb	42 lb	56 lb
Sack or coomb (4 bushels)	2¼ cwt	2 cwt	1½ cwt	2 cwt
Quarter (2 sacks)	4½ cwt	4 cwt	3 cwt	4 cwt
Weight per cubic foot	50 lb	44 lb	32 lb	44 lb
Cubic feet per ton	46	51	70	51

Harvesting. Threshing is the separation of the grains from the ears and straw. In *wheat* and *rye* the chaff is easily removed from the grain. In *barley*, only the awns are removed from the grain—the husk remains firmly attached to the kernel. In *oats* each grain kernel is surrounded by a husk which is fairly easily removed by a rolling process—as in the production of oatmeal; the chaff enclosing the grains in each spiklet threshes off. Most cereal crops in all parts of the country are now harvested by combine. The grain is bulk handled on most of the larger farms and stored in silos or loose on barn floors. Storage in *sacks* is still used on some farms.

Methods used for *drying* are set out below with usual moisture extraction rates in brackets:

(1) Various types of *continuous-flow driers:* hot air takes out the excess moisture and cold air then cools the grain (6% per hour).

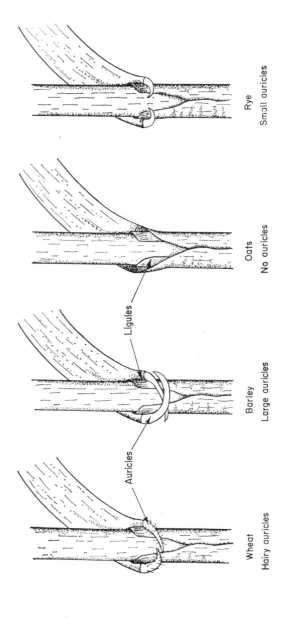

FIG. 36. Diagrams showing method of recognizing cereals in the leafy (vegetative) stage.

(2) *Batch driers*: drying similar to (1) but the grain is held in batches in special containers during the drying process (6% per hour in small types; 6% per day in silo types).

(3) *Ventilated silos or bins:* cold or slightly heated air is blown through the grain in the silo—this can be a slow process, especially in damp weather ($\frac{1}{3}$–1% per day).

(4) *Floor drying:* large volumes of slightly heated air are blown through the grain via ducts laid on or in the floor under the grain ($\frac{1}{3}$–1% per day).

(5) *Sack driers:* heated air is blown through the sacks of grain laid over holes in a platform or stacked to form a tunnel (1% per hour).

If possible, the grain should not be heated above the following *maximum* temperatures:

All grain intended for seed; malting barley up to 24% m.c.
120°F (49°C)

All grain intended for seed; malting barley above 24% m.c.
110°F (43°C)

Grain for milling for human food, e.g. wheat for flour
150°F (66°C)

Grain for stock feeding   180°F (82°C)

Safe moisture contents for storage of all grains:

In bulk (e.g. silos, loose on floor)	for long period	14% or less
In bulk	up to one month	14–16%
In sacks	for long period	16–18%
In sacks	a few weeks	18–20%

Only fully ripe grain in a very dry period is likely to be harvested in this country at 14% moisture. In a wet season, the moisture content may be over 30% and the grain may have to be dried in two or three stages.

Damp grains, above the limits set out above, will heat and may become useless. This heating is mainly due to the growth of moulds and respiration of the grain. Moulds, beetles and weevils may damage grain which is stored at a high temperature, e.g. grain not cooled properly after drying; or grain from the combine on a very hot day. Ideally, the grain should be cooled to 65°F (18°C)—this is difficult or impossible in hot weather.

Heating and destruction of dry grain in store several months after harvest may be caused by grain weevils and beetles. Insecticides can be used to fumigate silos and grain stores before harvest or applied to the grain when it is being stored. Special formulations of the insecticide malathion are commonly used for this purpose.

A recent development is the storage of damp grain, straight from the combine, in sealed silos. Fungi, grain respiration and insects use up the oxygen in the air spaces and give out carbon dioxide and the activity ceases when the oxygen is used up. The grain dies but the feeding value does not deteriorate whilst it remains in the silo. This method is best for damp grain of 18–24% moisture, but grain up to 30% or more may also be stored in this way although it is more likely to cause trouble when removing it from the silo, e.g. "bridging" above an auger. The damp grain is taken out of the silo as required for feeding. This method cannot be used for seed corn, malting barley, or wheat for flour milling.

Another recent development is the storage of damp grain by cooling it. Chilled air is blown through the grain and the higher the moisture content of the grain the lower the temperature must be, e.g.,

Moisture content of grain	18%	20%	22%
Temperature of grain (approx.)	45°F (7°C)	40°F (4½°C)	35°F (2°C)

This method is still in the experimental stage but the indications so far are that it is cheaper than drying and that the grain stores well, i.e. the germination is not affected and so could be used for seed, malting and milling.

Grain quality in cereals. Good quality grain is dry, clean, plump and has a thin skin or husk. It should have been well harvested and not musty, discoloured or overheated. If the grain is to be used for seed or malting (barley) the germination must be over 90% (preferably over 95%). A low nitrogen and high starch content (i.e. white

E

cross-section) is desirable in malting barley grains. Good bread-making quality wheat grains usually have a flinty (glossy) cross-section (see also N.I.A.B. leaflet on *Cereal Quality*).

Cereal *straw* may be *baled* for *bedding* (litter) or *feeding*; *burnt* in swath; or *ploughed-in* (after chopping or spreading).

Varieties. There are dozens of cereal varieties now on the market and new ones are introduced every year. However, there are only a few outstanding varieties of each cereal and these are described in the annual *Recommended Lists* from the National Institute of Agricultural Botany (N.I.A.B.). for England and Wales, and from the Agricultural Colleges in Scotland and the Ministry of Agriculture for Northern Ireland.

Seed-dressing. Cereal seed should be dressed with organo- mer-curial seed-dressings (2 oz bushel) to control fungus diseases such as covered *smuts* and *leaf-stripe*. A combined dressing, including insecticides, is useful for controlling *wireworms* and *wheat bulb fly*.

Fertilizers. These are usually combine-drilled with the seed, although the star-wheel mechanism used on most drills gives a very uneven distribution of fertilizer. A recent trend is to broadcast the fertilizer and use narrow row widths (4 in.) when sowing the seed; this reduces the labour costs and gives good results on fertile soils. All the fertilizer could be applied in the seed-bed with spring crops. With winter crops most of the nitrogen is top-dressed in the spring.

Average requirements:

60–80 units of N in drier, arable areas,
20–50 units of N in high rainfall and very fertile areas,
40 units of P_2O_5,
40 units of K_2O.

WHEAT

Wheat grain is used mainly for making *flour*. The type of flour produced varies with different varieties and the growing conditions. Most of the flour is used for making *biscuits* or *cakes* or for *blending* with bread-quality flour from North American wheats. The poorer quality grain and the by-products from white flour production, i.e. *bran* (skin of grain), and various inseparable mixtures of bran and flour (e.g. *weatings*) are fed to pigs, poultry and other stock. Some breakfast foods are made from wheat.

Wheat straw is used mainly for *bedding* but sometimes for *thatching* and *covering potato clamps* (*pits*).

Yield per acre

Average: about 30 cwt grain and 20–30 cwt straw.

Good: about 45 cwt grain and 30 cwt straw.

Soils and climate (pH should be higher than 5·5). Wheat is a deep-rooted plant which grows well on rich and heavy soils and in the sunnier eastern and southern parts of this country. Winter wheat can withstand most of the frosty conditions of this country but is easily killed by water-logged soil conditions.

Place in rotation. Wheat is the best cereal to grow when the soil is in a high state of fertility because it is the most resistant to "lodging" and yields best, e.g. it may be taken for 1 or 2 years after grassland and after potatoes. Winter wheat should not be grown continuously for many years because of likely failures due to fungus diseases such take-all and eye-spot.

Seed-beds. A fairly rough autumn seed-bed prevents "soil-capping" in a mild, wet winter and protects the base of the plants from cold frosty winds. In a difficult autumn, winter wheat may be successfully planted in a wet sticky seed-bed and usually produces a good crop. Spring wheat should only be planted in a good seed-bed.

Time of sowing

Winter wheat: late September–early February (October best).

Spring wheat: February–early May (early sowing best).

Methods of sowing (The seed should be 1–2 in. below the surface.)

(1) Drilling (a) Combine drill, 6–7 in. rows.

(b) Ordinary drill, 4–7 in. rows.

(2) Broadcasting, e.g. by hand, fiddle, spinner, aeroplane.

Seed-rate: winter wheat, $1\frac{1}{4}$–$1\frac{1}{2}$ cwt/acre; spring wheat $1\frac{1}{2}$–2 cwt/acre.

Varieties of wheat. Winter wheats usually yield better than spring varieties. Most of the modern varieties have red (brown) grain; the white (cream) grained varieties sprout too readily in a damp season. Most winter wheats must pass through a period of low temperatures and short days if they are to yield well—hence they should not be sown in the spring.

Popular varieties: winter, *Cappelle Deprez*; spring, *Opal*, (see also recommended lists.)

Fertilizers. General requirements in units per acre:

	N	P_2O_5	K_2O	For example
Winter wheat in seed-bed	0–30	30–50	30–50	2 cwt (10:20:20)
Spring top-dressing	40–80	—	—	3 cwt (21: 0: 0)
Spring wheat	40–80	30–40	30–40	4 cwt (20:10:10)
If 10 ton/acre F.Y.M. applied	20–30	—	—	

The lower figures for nitrogen shown in the table above would be adequate if the wheat was taken after grassland containing clovers or lucerne.

Spring grazing of winter wheat. If the crop is well forward in the spring and the soil is dry, it can provide useful grazing for sheep or cattle about late March. It should only be grazed once and should be top-dressed with nitrogen afterwards.

Harvesting. Winter wheat ripens before spring wheat; the crop is harvested in August and September. Indications of ripeness for harvesting:

(a) *Binder* — Straw: yellowish, all greenness gone.

Grain: in cheesy condition, firm but not hard.

(b) *Combine* (7–10 days later) — Straw: turning whitish; nodes shrivelled.

Grain: easily rubbed from ears, hard and dry.

Tillering of wheat (and other cereals). The production of side shoots (i.e. tillering) is a very important characteristic of cereals. Where the plants are thinly spaced more side shoots are likely to be produced than where they are close together and so a crop which is uneven in the seedling stage can even up considerably before harvest. All side shoots do not produce ears.

Lodging in wheat (and other cereals). Lodging (laying flat) is usually caused by wind and rain. It is most likely to occur when:

(a) the field is in an exposed situation,
(b) the variety is weak-strawed,
(c) excessive amounts of nitrogen are present in the soil, resulting in long weak straw and delayed ripening—this is likely to occur after a clovery ley or where too much nitrogen-fertilizer has been applied. A wet season makes matters worse,
(d) the straw is elongated and weakened due to shading when the plants are too dense or shaded by trees,
(e) the crop is attacked by the eye-spot fungus.

If the crop lodges when the straw is still green and growing the stems can bend at the nodes and grow upright again.

Lodging near maturity may not affect yield provided the pick-up reel mechanism on the combine is set properly when harvesting. It does, however, increase the cost of harvesting and grain quality may be spoiled.

A chemical (CCC) sprayed on young wheat plants reduces the length of straw and risk of lodging without reducing the yield.

BARLEY

Barley is a very important arable crop at the present time. The grain is used mainly for *feeding* to all classes of stock—especially pigs, dairy cows and intensively fed beef, and also for *malting* (about 20%).

The best quality grain (see p. 115) is usually sold for *malting*. In this process the wetted grain is sprouted, dried, and the *malt* produced is used for brewing beer, ale and stout, distilling whisky, or producing malt vinegar. Barley *straw* is usually used for bedding; some is fed to cattle.

Yield per acre

Average: 27 cwt grain and 20–30 cwt straw.
Good: 35 cwt grain and 35 cwt straw.

Soils and climate (pH should be about 6·5). Barley is a shallow-rooted crop which grows very well on chalk and limestone soils. It also does well on other types of soil provided they are well limed and drainage is good. On rich and heavy soils barley is likely to "lodge"—especially in a wet season—and the quality of the grain is unlikely to be suitable for malting.

Place in rotation. Usually taken at a stage where fertility is not high. Many farmers are now successfully growing spring barley continuously on the same fields.

Seed-beds. Winter barley should be planted in a fairly fine seed-bed with some lumps left on the surface. Spring barley needs a fine, uniform seed-bed; loose in top 2 in. and firm underneath.

Time and methods of sowing: similar to wheat.

Seed rate: 1¼ cwt/acre (1½ cwt for late sowings and in poor seed-beds; 1 cwt for feeding barley in good seed-beds).

Varieties. Spring barleys usually yield better and have better quality grain than winter barley. The main advantage of winter barley is that it ripens very early (usually in July).

Popular varieties

Winter: *Pioneer* and *Dea*;
Spring: Malting.   *Proctor, Maris Badger, Zephyr.*
        Feeding.   *Rika, Pallas, Impala, Vada.*

(See also recommended lists.)

Fertilizers. General requirements are similar to wheat except that the amount of nitrogen applied in spring to winter barley should be 40–60 units and to malting barley 20–50 units. Up to 100 units of nitrogen are required for continuous barley crops. F.Y.M. is seldom applied before planting barley.

Spring grazing of winter barley. It can be grazed like winter wheat but this is seldom done.

Harvesting

Winter barley ready July–early August.
Spring barley ready August–early September.

Barley is ready for harvesting by binder or combine when the straw has turned whitish and the ears are hanging downwards parallel to the straw. In a crop containing late tillers, harvesting should start when most of the crop is ready. Possible malting crops should be left to become as dead ripe as possible before harvesting. Harvesting of feeding barley is often started before the ideal stage—especially if a large acreage has to be harvested and the weather is uncertain. The ears of over-ripe crops and some varieties break off easily; this can result in serious losses.

The pick-up reel now fitted to most combines is very useful for picking up laid crops.

OATS

Oats are decreasing in importance because even the best varieties do not yield so well as barley and they are more difficult to harvest.

The best quality oat grains may be sold for making *oatmeal* which is used for making bread, oatcakes, porridge and for feeding chickens. Oats are the most suitable cereal for feeding to horses; they are very useful for sheep and cattle of all ages but because of the high fibre (husk) content are not very suitable for pigs.

Oat straw is very variable in quality. The best quality from leafy varieties is similar in feeding value to medium quality hay. Some short, stiff-strawed varieties have a similar feeding value to barley straw when grown in the warmer, drier parts of this country.

Yield per acre

Average: 22 cwt grain and 20–40 cwt straw.
Good: 33 cwt grain and 35 cwt straw.

Soils and climate. (pH should be about 5 or over—if too much lime is present, manganese deficiency (grey-leaf) may reduce yields).

Oats do best in the cooler and wetter northern and western parts of this country, but even in these areas they are being replaced by barley on many farms. They will grow on most types of soil and can withstand moderately acid conditions where wheat and barley would fail.

Place in rotation. Oats can be taken at almost any stage in a rotation of crops. If grown too often eelworms may cause a crop failure.

Seed-bed and *methods of sowing*: similar to wheat.

Time of sowing: winter oats, late September–October; *spring,* February–March.

Seed rate: 1½–2 cwt/acre.

Varieties. Winter varieties are not so frost hardy as winter wheat or barley; they usually yield better—especially in the drier districts—and are less likely to be damaged by *frit fly* than spring oats.

Popular varieties:

Winter: *Powys, Peniarth, Padarn;*
Spring: Mainly grain. *Condor, Astor,*
Grain and straw. *Ayr Commando, Maelor,* "*potato*" types.

(See also recommended lists.)

Fertilizers: similar to wheat, but less nitrogen.

40–50 units N.   30–40 units P_2O_5 30–40 units K_2O.

Spring grazing: that similar to wheat may be desirable if there is a risk of lodging because the grazing results in shorter straw.

Harvesting. There is still a high proportion of the oat crop cut with the binder—usually when the straw is still green or just turning yellow; this early cutting gives better quality straw and there is less shedding of grain.

If combined, the crop must be left until it is fully ripe; there is then a serious risk of shedding by high winds or if bad weather holds up the work.

RYE

Rye is grown on a small scale in this country for grain or very early grazing. The grain is used mainly for making rye crispbread; it is not in demand for feeding to livestock.

The long, tough straw is very good for thatching and bedding but is no good for feeding.

Yield per acre

Average: 20 cwt grain and 30 cwt straw.
Good: 30 cwt grain and 35 cwt straw.

Soils and climate. Rye will grow on poor, light acid soils and in dry districts where other cereals would fail. It is mainly grown in such conditions for grain because, on good soils, although the yields may be higher, it does not yield or sell so well as other cereals.

Rye is extremely frost hardy and will withstand much colder conditions than the other cereals.

Place in rotation. Rye can replace cereals in a rotation—especially where the fertility is not too high. It can be grown continuously on poor soils with occasional breaks of carrots, sugar-beet or leys. Grazing rye is usually taken as a catch crop before kale or roots.

Seed-beds and methods of sowing: similar to wheat.

Time of sowing: winter, September–October; *spring,* February–March. Grazing rye should, if possible, be sown in late August or early September.

Seed rate: for grain, $1\frac{1}{2}$ cwt/acre. Early sowing for grazing 1 cwt/acre.

Varieties. Most of the rye varieties grown now are winter types. Rye, unlike the other cereals, is cross-fertilized so varieties are difficult to maintain true to type and new seed should be bought in each year.

Popular varieties

Winter (grain): *King II, Petkus, Dominant*
Grazing: *Lovaszpatonai, Ovari.*

(See also N.I.A.B. list.)

Fertilizers. On light soils: For Grain.

40–50 units N   30–40 P_2O_5 30–40 K_2O.

Same amounts used for grazing rye on better soils. The nitrogen is normally applied as a top-dressing in February.

Spring grazing. The special varieties for early spring grazing (late February–March) can be grazed at least twice if the grazing is started before the plants develop hollow stems. Once-grazed crops can be left to harvest as grain which is usually sold for seed.

Harvesting. Rye is normally the first of the cereal crops to ripen. It is cut with the binder or combine near the dead ripe stage when the grain is hard and dry and the straw turning from a greyish to whitish appearance. The ears sprout very readily in a wet harvest season. If the crop is grown for its high quality straw it should be cut with the binder before the grain develops and so the straw is not damaged by threshing.

MIXED CORN CROPS

Mixtures of cereals (*dredge corn*) are grown in some areas— particularly in the south-west. The commonest type is a mixture of barley and oats in various proportions with a total seed rate of about $1\frac{3}{4}$ cwt/acre. The yield of grain is usually better than if either crop was grown alone. Varieties must be chosen which ripen at the same time.

Sometimes cereals and peas or beans are mixed (*mashlum*)— this type can be used for silage or grain.

Winter and spring mixtures are used.

Growing and harvesting: grain—similar to oats; silage—forage harvester.

MAIZE

A small acreage of maize is grown in the southern half of this country—mainly for making into *silage*. Maize is not suitable for grain production here because of the difficulty of harvesting and drying in an average or wet season. There is a limited market for the cobs of the *sweetcorn* varieties as a vegetable. Maize stover (leaves and stems) can be fed to cattle before the cobs develop—this may be useful in the drier south-eastern counties in a dry season.

Yield per acre

Silage: 10–25 tons/acre.

Vegetable cobs: up to 30,000/acre.

Soils and climate. Maize does best on fertile loam soils (pH above 5·5). It is susceptible to frost damage in spring and autumn; growth is very slow when the temperature is below 50°F (10°C) and so the growing season is restricted. It likes plenty of sunshine.

Place in rotation. Usually taken as part of the "root break" but may be grown continuously on a convenient field.

Seed-bed: as for a spring cereal.

Seed rate: 30 lb (small seed)–40 lb (large seeded varieties).

Sowing: drilled about 2 in. deep in rows 28–36 in. apart. (a plant population of about 50,000 acre is desirable for silage).

Time of sowing: late April or early May.

Varieties. A large number are available (see N.I.A.B. leaflet No. 17). The medium maturity group is the most satisfactory type for silage.

Fertilizer. If possible, 10–15 tons/acre F.Y.M.; also 40–60 units each of N, P_2O_5 and K_2O.

The response to fertilizers is often disappointing.

Problems.

(a) *Rooks* can destroy a crop in the seedling stage. The remedy is black cotton on light sticks 3–4 ft high and 8–11 yd apart each way.

(b) *Weeds* can smother the crop in the young stages of growth. Control is best achieved by spraying the field with atrazine as soon as possible after planting. A less satisfactory alternative is 2,4-D applied when crop is about 6 in. high.

Harvesting and *silage.* Cut and chop with flail-harvester when the grain in the "cobs" is in the "cheesy" stage—usually late September or October. No additives are necessary when making the silage. Compared with grass silage, it is low in protein.

Pulse Crops

Pulse crops are *legumes* which have edible seeds; the main ones grown in this country are the various types of *beans* and *peas*. Bacteria on the roots of these crops can fix nitrogen, so, normally, they do not require nitrogen fertilizers and the following crop benefits from nitrogen left in the soil.

Beans and peas are useful, protein-rich grains for blending with cereals for feeding farm stock, but yields may be disappointing and harvesting troublesome. At present, peas, are mainly grown for human consumption in the canned, quick-frozen, or dried state; beans for human consumption (canned, frozen and dried) are increasing in importance as a farm crop which can be mechanically harvested, e.g. dwarf stringless beans.

The smaller (tick) beans and maple peas are popular for pigeon feeding.

Beans and peas can be used in mixtures with cereals for ensilage.

Stock-feeding beans usually grow well on heavy soils and loams, whereas peas, French and runner beans prefer the medium and lighter soils.

Beans or peas provide a useful break between cereal crops but should not be grown in successive years because of fungus diseases and pests—although climbing French (kidney) beans are sometimes grown on the same site for several years where fixed support wires have been erected.

The introduction of improved varieties, chemical control of weeds and pests such as aphids, may result in a greater acreage being grown for stock feeding.

BEANS

Types

    (a) *Stock-feeding* (*Field beans*)

        (1) *Winter beans.* These are not very frost hardy and are more susceptible to "chocolate spot" disease but usually yield much better and ripen 2–4 weeks earlier than spring beans.

(2) *Spring beans*. There are two main types—*tick* (*tic*) beans—small seeds and *horse* beans—large seeds.

(See N.I.A.B. leaflet on *Field Beans*)

Yields per acre.

Average: winter beans 18 cwt grain and 30 cwt straw.
Good: winter beans 30 cwt grain and 45 cwt straw.

(b) *Human consumption*. Varieties of broad, French (kidney), and runner beans are popular. Some are grown under contract for canning, quick-freezing or artificial drying and may be mechanically harvested. Growing and harvesting are not dealt with here (see MAFF bulletin No. 87, *Beans*).

Soils and climate. Field beans grow well on clay soils and heavy loams provided they are well drained and limed (pH above 6·0–the nodule bacteria work is better when pH is high). Soils rich in organic matter and nitrogen usually produce too much straw and poor yields of grain.

The French and runner beans prefer loams and lighter soils—especially where irrigation is possible.

Winter beans are risky to grow north of the Midlands because of possible frost damage. French beans are easily damaged by frost.

Seed-bed: deeper, but otherwise similar to cereals.

Sowing. Winter beans do best if sown in early October at 2 cwt/acre. Spring beans should be sown in late February or early March at $1\frac{3}{4}$–$2\frac{1}{4}$ cwt/acre.

Spring beans are often sown in wide rows (18–24 in.) so that weeds can be controlled by inter-row cultivations, and the crop is not damaged by tractor wheels when sprayed to control aphids. Winter and spring beans may be sown in narrow rows with the corn drill and annual weeds controlled by pre-emergence spraying with simazine.

The usual depth of sowing is 2–3 in.

In difficult conditions the beans may be ploughed in (not more than 4 in. deep) or broadcast on the ploughing and covered by harrows.

Fertilizers: 10 tons/acre F.Y.M. if available *or* 40 units P_2O_5 and 80 units K_2O broadcast or placed in bands about 2 in. from the seed.

Treatment during growing season. Spray with systemic insecticide in June to control black fly (aphid) on spring beans.

Honey bees are very helpful in the fertilization of beans and increase the yield considerably; one hive per acre spread round the field should be adequate.

Harvesting. Winter beans are usually ready for harvesting in August and spring beans in September or October. They ripen unevenly—the lower pods are first to mature.

The crop is ready for cutting with the binder when the pods about half way up the stem have turned black and the scar (hilum) where the bean is attached to the pod is also black. At this stage there are green pods and leaves on the plant but these will ripen during the 2–4 weeks in the stooks before they are stacked.

Most crops are now harvested by combine when the leaves have withered and nearly all the pods are ripe.

The straw cut early with the binder is reasonably good for feeding; but combined straw is useless.

Some grain is lost by shedding by both methods—sheep will pick up beans from the stubbles.

Binder-harvested beans are seldom threshed before the following January.

Drying and Storage. Combined beans may require drying before storage. They should be dried carefully—preferably in two stages—if moisture content is much over 20%. Storage conditions and bushel weight are the same as wheat (64 lb/bushel).

PEAS

Type 1. *For human consumption* (*white-flowered*)

    (a) Threshed (dry) peas—sold loose, in packets, or canned; marrowfats (e.g. *Zelka*); large blues (e.g. *Rondo*).

        Yield: average, 18 cwt/acre; good, 28 cwt/acre.

    (b) Vining peas—for canning fresh ("garden peas"), quick-freezing or artificial drying.

        These are grown under contract and seed is supplied by

the purchasing firms—there is a wide range of dwarf varieties including early, medium and late types.

Yield: average, 28 cwt/acre; good, 48 cwt/acre.

(c) Pulling peas—sold as fresh peas in the pod.

There are many varieties and they are mainly grown as a market garden crop.

Yield: average, 3 tons/acre; good, 4½ tons/acre.

Type 2. For stock-feeding and pigeons (reddish flowers), e.g.

Maple peas (brown and yellow mottled grain).

Yield: average, 18 cwt/acre; good, 28 cwt/acre.

Soils and climate. Peas grow best on loam and lighter types of soil, provided they are well drained and limed (pH well above 5·5). The threshed peas require good harvest weather for drying in the field and so are grown in the drier eastern counties. Vining and pulling peas are not so dependent on dry weather at harvest and are grown in most of the arable areas—including the West Midlands.

Seed-bed. The peas should be drilled about 2 in. deep in a loose tilth. On the lighter soils they may be drilled into well broken furrow slices or after one harrowing.

Sowing. Narrow rows (about 7 in. apart) are popular now, although wider rows (14 in. or more) are still used and weeds controlled by inter-row cultivations.

Seed rate: average, 2 cwt/acre of chemically dressed seed (e.g. TMTD, captan).

Fertilizer. Average conditions 30 units P_2O_5, 70 units K_2O (ideally, "placed" 2–3 in. from the seed).

Time of sowing

Threshed peas: early March.

Vining peas: February–May, according to the factory fieldsman's instructions (usually based on a "heat units" system).

Pulling peas: January–April.

Weed control. Wild oats can be controlled by *propham* or TCA applied in the seed-bed or *barban* at early seedling stage. For annual weeds, spray with DNBP when peas are 3–10 in. high or MCPB when peas have 3–6 leaves (factory permission required).

Light harrowing (on a dry day) in the early stages of growth (2–4 in.) will kill some annual weed seedlings.

Harvesting. Peas are usually cut with special pea-cutters or mowers fitted with special lifters. The crop is left in windrows.

Threshed and stock-feed peas are ready when the vines and pods have turned a yellow or light brown colour and before the seed starts to shed. After partly drying on the ground the crop can be put on tripods, 4-poles, or racks to complete drying. Alternatively, it may be allowed to dry fully in the windrows and then be stacked or picked up and threshed with a combine. If drying is necessary it must be done slowly and at a low temperature (110°F: 43°C). The storage moisture content is the same as for cereals.

Vining peas are cut when the crop is still green and just starting to lose colour. The haulms (and pods) are put through a special vining machine which separates the peas from the pods. These machines are usually fixed at central sites, but mobile machines are now being used in the field. The peas are rushed off to the factory for canning, freezing or drying and the haulms can be used for silage or dried as hay.

Pulling peas require a large gang of casual labour to do the job quickly while the crop is in a fresh, sweet condition.

Linseed and Flax

These are different varieties of the same plant. *Linseed* varieties (e.g. *Dakota, Valuta*) have been specially selected for producing a high yield of seed for *oil* extraction (and cattle cake). *Flax* varieties (e.g. *Liral Prince*) have been selected for long stems and *fibre* production—for making *linen*.

Both crops were very important during and after the last war but flax is not grown in this country now. They both prefer the medium to heavier types of soil and will grow in a wide range of climatic conditions.

Both crops like a fine, firm seed-bed, and can be sown in March or April in narrow rows (7 in. or less) and about 1 in. deep, with about 3 cwt/acre of compound fertilizer, e.g. 12:12:18.

Seed rate: linseed, 50–70 lb/acre; flax 90–110 lb/acre.

Harvesting linseed. This is ready when the seeds in the bolls are brown and shiny. It is cut with a binder, stooked, stacked and threshed in dry weather, or alternatively, cut with a mower and combined from the swath.

Yield of seed: 10–20 cwt/acre.

Harvesting flax. This is ready when leaves have fallen off the lower 12–15 in. of stem. The crop is pulled by hand or with special machines and tied in beets (sheaves). These are later *retted* (partly rotted) in dams on the farm or in tanks at the factory. This allows the flax fibres to be easily scutched (separated) from the woody stem core.

Yield of fibre 40–70 stone/acre, also 3–4 cwt/acre of seed if this removed before the retting process.

Potatoes

Uses. Potatoes are mainly used for human consumption. About 200 lb/head are eaten every year as *boiled* or *baked potatoes, chips, crisps,* etc.

Good quality ware potato tubers

(a) are not damaged or diseased,
(b) have smooth clean skins which are easily peeled,
(c) have flesh which does not blacken,
(d) are of reasonable size.

Popular varieties (See also N.I.A.B. recommended list.)

Earlies	*Main crop*
Arran Pilot (white skin)	Majestic (white skin)
Homeguard (white skin)	King Edward (red and white skin)
Craig's Royal (red and white skin)	Kerr's Pink (pink skin)
Red Craig's Royal (Red skin)	Red skin (favoured in Scotland)
	Record (grown on contract for crisps)

	Earlies	Main crop	Seed
Yield of tubers per acre	4–12 tons	8–16 tons	7–10 tons
Seed rate per acre	25–30 cwt	15–20 cwt	25 cwt
Time of planting	Feb.–March	April	April
Time of harvesting	June–July	Sept.–Oct.	Aug.–Oct.

Suitable soils. Main crops grow best on deep loam soils. Earlies do best on early light soils in areas free from late frosts.

Place in rotation. This may be taken at any stage but maincrops or seed should not be grown more often than two years in eight because root eelworms may build up in the soil.

Seed-bed preparation. Early, deep ploughing is necessary to allow for frost action. Deep cultivation, harrowing, and, if necessary, rotary cultivation are required to produce a fine deep tilth without losing too much moisture.

Seed potatoes. The "seed" which the farmer plants is a tuber not a true seed. This is a vegetative method of reproduction and all healthy plants of the same variety are alike. New varieties are produced by sowing the true seeds found in the green tomato-like fruits which develop from the flowers of some varieties.

The best quality "seed" tubers are grown in areas where green-flies (aphids) are not common. The aphids spread virus diseases such as *leaf roll* and *mosaic* from diseased to healthy plants. Parts of Scotland and Northern Ireland and hill areas in England and Wales are suitable for growing potatoes for "seed". Stock seed (SS), class A and class H, are grades of seed. Recently, some lowland farmers have been using insecticides to control the aphids in their crops and so they do not need to buy new "seed" every year.

Sprouting of tubers before planting. This is necessary with earlies and desirable for main crops and seed crops. The tubers are placed in special sprouting boxes which allow light to reach them. The boxed seed is stored during the winter in glasshouses which can be heated to prevent frost damage or in sheds fitted with warm-white fluorescent tube lighting. The rate of growth of the sprouts is increased by raising the temperature; the size of the sprout is controlled by light—short, sturdy sprouts are formed in well-lighted sheds. The main advantages are: earlier growth, less risk of blight, higher yields, earlier harvesting, and rogues can be removed from seed crops because they have different sprouts.

Tubers to be used for seed production should be sprouted late—this results in more sprouts per tuber and so more seed size tubers in the crop. Tubers sprouted early usually produce only one sprout per tuber—this is desirable for earlies.

The temperature range for sprouting is 5°C (41°F)–18°C (65°F).

Planting. This is done either by:

(a) mechanical planters (2–4 row) which may be automatic or may be assisted by workers who place the seed tubers in cups or tubes,

Or

(b) by hand; ridges are opened by a ridging plough, the tubers are planted by hand, and the ridges split to cover the tubers.

Spacing of tubers:

(a) Distance between ridges: earlies, 24–26 in; main crop, 26–30 in.

(b) Distance between the seed tubers (setts) depends on the average size of the tubers and the rate per acre planted. Setts averaging 2 oz (size of hen's egg) planted in 28 in. rows at the rate of 20 cwt/acre would be spaced 12–13 in. apart.

Manuring. Potato crops will benefit from F.Y.M. if it is available. Usual dressing is about 15 tons/acre. This is either ploughed-in during the autumn or put in the ridges in the spring.

The fertilizers may be broadcast over the open ridges before planting or "placed" in bands by the mechanical planter. The amounts required *per acre* may be summarized as follows:

	Units per acre			Examples of compounds
	N	P_2O_5	K_2O	
With 10 tons F.Y.M.	80	80	120	7 cwt (12:12:18)
Without F.Y.M.	100	100	150	10 cwt (10:10:15)

Nitrogen should be reduced to about 50 units after good grass-land. Potash could be increased to 200 units on low potash soils.

Weeds, by tradition, are controlled by cultivations and ridging after planting but the frequent passage of rubber-tyred tractors tends to produce clods in the ridges and this hinders mechanical harvesting. The cultivations also damage the potato roots and stolons and allow moisture to escape from the soil.

Chemical weed control (see p. 213) with the minimum or no cultivations after planting is now becoming common practice.

Some farmers are now growing potatoes "on the flat" (in beds about 4½ ft wide) instead of ridges; yields are increased but harvesting is difficult on the heavier soils.

The new tubers in the ridges must be kept covered with soil to protect them from damage by (a) "greening"—due to exposure to light, and (b) blight—due to spores falling onto the tubers from diseased leaves.

Blight. This is one of the worst fungus diseases attacking the potato crop. It can seriously reduce yield by killing off the tops (foliage) early. It can also cause rotting of the tubers before or during storage. Some varieties are more resistant to blight than others.

Spraying or dusting with special fungicides can partly control the spread of the disease on the leaves. Chemical or mechanical destruction of the "tops" before the disease kills them completely can reduce the risk of spread of the disease to the tubers. The disease can spread very quickly on the foliage in damp, warm weather.

Harvesting. Mechanical harvesters are still in the development stage. Some machines work well in various soil conditions and can save a lot of backache! The slow speed of working, mechanical damage to the tubers, and amount of manual labour required are the main criticisms of present-day machines.

Hand-picking is still the main method used. If a *spinner* is used for exposing the tubers then only one row can be picked up at a time. It is more efficient to lift a number of rows ahead of the pickers (one row for each picker). This can be done by several types of *lifters*, e.g. *elevator digger, swinging-sieve type* or *potato plough*.

The pickers put the potatoes into baskets and these are then emptied into trailers alongside or into *stillages* (boxes or containers which can be mechanically handled).

Storage. The tubers may be stored in a clamp in the field and covered with a good layer of straw and then 6–12 in. of soil to prevent frost damage. However, it is now common practice to store indoors in frost-proof sheds with ventilating ducts under the heap. Forced ventilation and the use of chemicals can control sprouting in the spring.

Grading. The stored tubers are usually riddled (graded or sorted) during the winter or early spring. The best potatoes (ware) are separated from the chats (small tubers), diseased, damaged, over-sized and mis-shapen tubers.

Sugar-beet

The sugar which is extracted from the crop supplies this country with 25% of its total sugar consumption.

It is grown on contract for the British Sugar Corporation which has eighteen factories in the British Isles. A contract price per ton of washed beet containing a standard percentage of sugar is fixed each year. A bonus or deduction is made if the sugar content is above or below the standard. The average sugar content is about $15\frac{1}{2}\%$.

Apart from its sugar, sugar-beet has two useful by-products:

(1) Beet tops—a very succulent food, but which must be fed wilted.

(2) Beet pulp—the residue of the roots after the sugar has been extracted; an excellent feed for stock.

Yield of roots per acre: 14–16 tons, which yields over 2 tons of sugar.

Yield of tops per acre: 10–12 tons. The stock farmer prefers the heavier yielding large topped varieties.

Seed rate per acre: 4–6 lb of rubbed and graded seed or 12–15 lb of natural seed.

Time of sowing: mid-March–mid-April.

Time of harvesting: end of September to December.

Varieties

The N.I.A.B. recommended list, and the factory field officer will help in deciding upon the variety to be grown. There are many different varieties and they can be grouped according to the yield of roots, the sugar percentage, and their resistance to bolting, i.e. running to seed in the year of sowing. This is influenced by a cold spell in the three- to four-leaf stage of the plant. Bolting is highly undesirable, as the roots become woody with a low sugar content. Varieties with a high resistance to bolting should be used for early sowing and in colder districts.

Climate and soils. Sugar-beet is a sun-loving crop which will not grow well when there is too much rain and cloud.

It can be grown on the majority of soils, except heavy clays, which are usually too wet and sticky, and stony soils, which make cultivation and harvesting difficult.

Place in rotation. As long as the land is reasonably clean of weeds, the place in rotation is not so important these days. But by law, beet must not be grown too frequently on the same land because of the build up of eelworm.

Seed-bed. The importance of a good seed-bed for sugar-beet cannot be over-emphasized. The success or failure of the crop can, to a great extent, depend on the seed-bed. It must be deep yet firm, fine and level.

Manuring

(1) *F.Y.M.:* 10–12 tons of well rotted manure per acre; applied in the autumn.

(2) *Salt:* 3–5 cwt/acre broadcast a few weeks before sowing. This should give an extra 3 cwt of sugar per acre.

Other plant foods required can be summarized as follows:

	Units per acre			Examples of compounds
	N	P_2O_5	K_2O	
With F.Y.M. and salt	80	40	70	4 cwt (20:10:20)
Without F.Y.M. but including salt	100	50	100	5 cwt (20:10:20)

Kainit can be used at 5 cwt/acre instead of potash and salt. It should be applied some weeks before sowing the seed.

The fertilizer may be broadcast and worked into the soil during seed-bed preparations, or it can be placed in bands near the seed. This latter will give earlier growth, and a probable increase in yield.

The seed and sowing. The so-called beet seed is really a cluster of seeds fused together, and it usually produces more than one plant when it germinates. Therefore, seed is now used which has been separated from the cluster. This is known as rubbed and graded seed (size 8–10/64ths in.). The use of this seed increases the proportion of single plants by as much as 10–15%, compared with "natural" seed (the seed cluster), and certainly makes subsequent singling much easier.

Monogerm seed, from which only one plant will grow, has now been produced. To date, germination has not been very high, and those plants which have grown are not as good as existing varieties. But these difficulties will be overcome, and eventually this will be the only type of seed used.

The crop should be sown at 18–22 in. apart, and great care must be taken to see that the drills or rows of plants are as straight and evenly spaced as possible because of subsequent inter-row work.

Shallower sowing will aid quicker germination; ¾–1 in. is ideal with a well prepared seedbed. A press wheel fitted immediately behind the seed coulter effectively compresses the soil over the seed, and in dry weather this will help germination.

Treatment during the growing period. The crop should emerge in weed-free conditions following pre-emergence chemical weed control treatment. But as soon as the seedlings can be seen as continuous lines across the field, steerage hoeing should also be carried out to assist in weed control, and to ease the work of singling.

(1) *Singling* (thinning). Ideally this should be done at the four- to five-leaf stage of the plant. Delaying it much after this will certainly mean a reduction in final yield.

(a) *Singling by hand* is often done at piece work rates. The final average distance apart of the plants in the row must depend upon the row widths, i.e. rows of 20 in. apart—plants thinned to 10 in. apart, or rows of 22 in. apart—plants thinned to 9 in. apart. This will give a plant population approaching the ideal 30,000 to the acre.

(b) *Mechanical singling*. Gapping machines are sometimes used which leave the plants in bunches at regular intervals in the rows. This will be followed by hand singling.

The "down-the-row" thinner type of machine which knocks out plants at regular intervals as it moves down the row, if correctly used can completely mechanize the singling operation.

An even row is of great importance if mechanical thinning is to be successful. It is usually carried out in two stages. The first thinning treatment reduces the plants in the row by approximately 50%, and the second (a few days after the first) reduces the plant to about the correct spacing in the row, although hand trimming will usually be necessary to follow.

Hand trimming, combined with flat hoeing, will also be necessary after hand singling, usually 3–4 weeks later, to tidy up the rows (chopping out any doubles) and hoe out weeds between the plants.

Further inter-row work can be carried out to check the weeds, and these hoeings may be continued until the beet leaves finally meet across the rows, but if it is rather dry, too much working of the soil must be avoided.

(2) *Spraying against virus yellows*. It may be necessary to spray the crop to kill the aphids which spread virus yellows (see p. 244).

Harvesting. In theory, early November is the right time to harvest the beet crop. Although it is still slightly increasing in weight the sugar percentage is beginning to fall off.

But, of course, if all beet were delivered at this time there would be tremendous congestion at the factory. Therefore a permit delivery system is used, whereby each grower is given dated loading permits which operate from the end of September until about the end of January. It means that growers must be prepared to have their beet delivered to the factory at intervals throughout the period upon receiving prior notice from the factory.

Lifting can be carried out either by hand or machine. Whichever method is used, topping must be done accurately (see Fig. 37). Overtopping can result in a serious loss of yield, and undertopping means paying extra carriage for unwanted material.

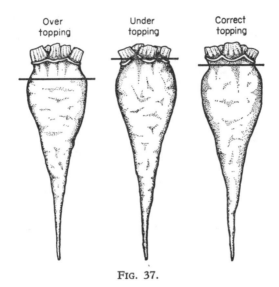

FIG. 37.

Hand harvesting. The crop is loosened in the row using a beet lifter or plough. This is followed by pulling (two rows at a time), knocking the beet together, and laying out in rows for topping.

By machine. More than 70% of the sugar-beet crop in this country is now harvested mechanically.

Most machines top and lift the beet, and deliver it into trailers. Many can be fitted with "top savers" which leave the tops in clean condition for subsequent feeding.

The majority of harvesters are now reasonably efficient, but the heavier the soil, the less efficient they become!

Mangolds

The mangold is grown for feeding to cattle and sheep in the more southerly parts of the country, where it is a more certain cropper than swedes and turnips. In the wetter and cooler regions the latter crops are preferable. It contains less than 14% dry matter, and is quite susceptible to frost injury. Because of this, the crop is harvested before it is mature. But it should not be fed until after Christmas, when it has ripened off in the clamp. The tops are of no value. The growing of mangolds is similar to sugar-beet as regards soil and climate, seed-bed preparations, and general fertilizer treatment.

Yield per acre: 20–30 tons.

Seed rate per acre: 8–10 lb.

Sowing: April to early May, in rows 22–24 in. apart. Unnecessarily wide rows reduce the yield; the ultimate aim should be 25,000 plants to the acre.

Varieties: Globes, Tankards (oblong-shaped), Longs, Intermediates (in shape between the Globe and the Long).

Treatment during the growing period can follow the same pattern as for sugar-beet, although singling is usually started when the plants are in the two- to three-leaf stage.

Harvesting. November is the normal time to harvest the crop. They are simply pulled out, and because they "bleed" very easily, the tops (not the crowns) are either cut or twisted off. The roots are left untrimmed.

After a period of "sweating out" in the field in small heaps covered with leaves, the mangolds must be carefully clamped. They should be built up as large as they can be conveniently heaped, and then covered with a good layer of straw. This will be sufficient in sheltered areas away from frost, but otherwise soil on top of the straw will have to be used in addition.

Fodder Beet

This plant has been bred from selections from sugar-beet and mangolds. It aroused great interest in this country during and just after the Second World War because of its value in pig feeding. It has a higher dry matter content than the mangold, and it is quite useful in the fattening of pigs, although it has declined markedly in popularity in recent years. Fodder beet can be fed immediately after lifting, and the tops after wilting are also valuable. Its growing is very similar to that of mangolds.

Turnips and Swedes

They are the most widely grown root crops in the northern and western regions of the country. In appearance the difference between the two crops is that turnips have hairy, grass-green leaves which arise direct from the bulb itself, and swedes have smooth, ashy-green leaves which grow out from an extended stem or "neck". Nutritionally swedes are more valuable than turnips as they have a higher, dry matter content. The turnip has a shorter growing period and some varieties can be grown very usefully as catch crops.

Both are extremely valuable for cattle and sheep and, depending on the variety grown, they can be used as table vegetables.

Yield per acre: turnips, 20 tons; swedes, 20–35 tons.

Seed rate per acre:

1–4 lb (lower amount with the precision drill) in rows 22–24 in. apart. White turnips can be broadcast at 4–6 lb.

All seed should be dressed with gamma-BHC as a protection against flea-beetle.

Time of sowing: mid-April to the end of June. White turnips as a catch crop at any time from April to late August.

Climate and soil. The crops like a cool, moist climate without too much sunshine. Most soils (except heavy clays) are suitable.

Varieties

Varieties	Feed Value	Remarks
Turnips White-fleshed	Low	Heavy croppers; poor keepers; can be grown as a catch crop, as well as a main crop.
Soft-yellows	Intermediate	Can be grown for both stock and table.
Yellow-fleshed	High	Slowest to mature; keeping quality good; require fertile conditions for best results.
Swedes (grouped according to skin colour)		
Light-purple	Generally low	Normally quickest to mature and heaviest yielder.
Dark-purple	Medium to high	Not heavy yielding. Highly resistant to frost damage. Suited more to conditions in Scotland.
Green	High	Later to mature and fairly hardy, many varieties are resistant to club-root disease.
Bronze	Very mixed varieties as regards yield, time of maturity and hardiness.	

For more details of varieties see the N.I.A.B. recommended list.

Seedbed. A fine, firm and moist seed-bed is necessary to get the plant quickly established. In very wet districts the crops can, with advantage, be sown on the ridge (see p. 77).

Manuring. F.Y.M.—10–15 tons/acre—is applied in the autumn. This is especially important for lighter soils as it improves the water-holding capacity.

Other plant foods required can be summarized as follows.

	Units per acre			Examples of compounds
	N	P_2O_5	K_2O	
With F.Y.M.	40	40–60	40	4 cwt (10:10:10)
Without F.Y.M.	40–80	80–90	80	4 cwt (10:20:20)

The lower amount of nitrogen is used in wetter areas and more phosphate is needed on heavier soils.

Lime is most essential. Soil pH should be above 6·0. Finger and toe disease can be prevalent under acid conditions.

Treatment during the growing period. The inter-row cultivations carried out on the crop for weed control should follow the same lines as with most root crops, and these, with the use of chemicals, will keep the crop clean (see p. 217). If the crop has not been precision drilled it will be advisable to rough single to 8–10 in. apart. This is normally done at the two- to three-leaf stage with main crops. With a good initial stand of plants, mechanical thinning can reduce the time spent on this arduous job, although with precision drilled crops there is an increasing practice not to thin the crop at all.

Harvesting turnips. The main crop is ready for lifting and feeding in October when the outer leaves begin to decay. They can be stored in one main clamp (the leaves may be left on) in a similar way to mangolds.

In mild districts yellow turnips can be left growing in the field and removed as required, or they may be stored in small, roughly covered heaps in the field.

Both white and yellow turnips, but particularly white turnips, are often grazed off in the field.

Harvesting swedes. In most districts swedes are lifted about November, before they are fully matured. It is therefore advisable to allow roots to ripen off in a clamp to minimize scouring when later feeding to stock. In fact, in mild districts they may be left growing to mature in the field. Swedes, like turnips, can also be grazed off in the field.

Kale

Kale is grown for feeding to livestock in the winter months. It can be fed either (1) on the field, or (2) it can be cut and carted off for feeding green or making into silage, and in these cases a heavier yielding crop is needed.

Yield per acre: 15–30 tons (about 7 tons per foot in height of thick crop).

Time of sowing: end of March–mid-July. Early sowing gives heavier crops but these are more susceptible to frost damage.

Seed rate per acre: 1–3 lb *drilled* (18–24 in. rows); 4–6 lb *broadcast*.

The seed should be dressed with gamma-BHC as a protection against flea-beetle.

Types of kale

Marrow stem	4–5 ft. tall. Thick stems and large leaves. Produces the heaviest crops, but not winter hardy. Use before the new Year.
Thousand-head	2–3 ft tall. Much branched plant; numerous small leaves. Hardier, but less palatable than marrow stem. N.B. Canson kale is a dwarf variety of thousand-head kale; it is useful for feeding to sheep early in the year.
Hungry gap and rape kales	Are not true kales, but rapes. Low-growing plants. Produce a second crop of leaves in Feb.–March period.

With any type of kale it is important to choose a reliable variety within the type.

The N.I.A.B. recommended list will give advice on varieties.

Climate and soil. Kale is a very adaptable crop, although under very dry conditions it may be a little difficult to get it well established. For folding, it is preferable to grow it under drier, lighter soil conditions, or on well drained soils.

Manuring. F.Y.M.—up to 20 tons/acre—is applied in the autumn. It is especially important when a heavy yielding crop is the aim.

Other plant foods required can be summarized as follows:

	Units per acre			Examples of compounds
	N	P_2O_5	K_2O	
With F.Y.M.	80–100	60	50	5c. (20:10:10)
Without F.Y.M.	100–120	80	80	8c. (15:10:10)

The lower amount of nitrogen is for the folded crop. The fertilizer is usually applied during final seed-bed preparations. Although placement of fertilizer and seed can be carried out there is no great improvement in final yield.

Seed-bed. A fine, firm, and clean seed-bed is required.

Treatment during the growing period. With drilled crops, steerage hoeing may have to be carried out a number of times from an early stage, but the new herbicide "Semeron" has eased the problem of keeping the crop clean of weeds (see pp. 216 and 217).

If necessary, the crop should be dusted against flea-beetles.

The drilled crop is not often singled. With an unthinned crop a higher proportion of leaf to stem is obtained which produces more succulent plants. Sometimes the crop is harrowed across to thin a rather thick crop.

Utilizing the crop. With cattle, grazing in the field using the electric fence avoids the laborious job of cutting and carting the crop. But light or well drained soils are essential, otherwise both stock and soil will suffer.

To avoid wet and sticky conditions which normally get worse towards the end of the year, the tendency these days is to start feeding kale to dairy cows much earlier in the autumn, although in a mild season it will continue to grow on well into early winter.

If strip-grazing is not possible, the forage-harvester may be used to chop the crop coarsely and blow it into a trailer, or it can be cut with an old mower.

Cabbages

Cabbages have a wide range of uses. They are a useful food for all classes of stock and, when suitable varieties are grown, high value crops can be produced for human consumption. These can be fed to stock when the market price is too low.

Cabbages prefer moist, heavy soils, and seasons with plenty of rainfall, but apart from this the same growing conditions suit cabbage as kale. They respond to plenty of fertilizer, but too much nitrogen (not more than 90 units) can cause the hearts to split.

Varieties. There are a large number of varieties which can be roughly grouped as follows:

	Sown	Planted out	Ready for consumption	
Early	March May August	April, May June, July Following April September	August–September October onwards July March–June	Can be used for stock and human consumption.
Late *or* Maincrop	August August	Following April October	September July onwards	Chiefly used for stock feeding.

A reliable variety should be chosen within these groups, and the N.I.A.B. recommended list will give details of varieties of flat poll cabbage. The seed is normally sown in specially prepared seed-beds. 1 lb of seed gives sufficient plants for planting 1 acre. 3 cwt of superphosphate should be broadcast before sowing. For planting out, a transplanter can be used. They are best planted on the square, i.e. approximately 2 ft between the plants and 2 ft between the rows. This will help in later cultivations. The treatment during the growing period consists of thorough, but not too deep inter-row cultivations, until further work would damage the crop, although in dry seasons the number of cultivations should be reduced in order to conserve moisture. It should be possible to obtain a yield of at least 30 tons/acre, and with generous manurial treatment in good moist seasons, yields of up to 60 tons/acre are not uncommon.

Carrots

The common yellow carrots may be grown on contract for canning or quick-freezing but most of the crop is sold as a vegetable—either as fully grown clean roots or as bunches of young carrots. Unsaleable and surplus roots can be fed to stock (usually cattle); the white cattle carrots are not grown in this country now.

Yield of roots: average, 12 tons/acre; good, 25 tons/acre.

Soils and climate. The climate in most parts of this country is suitable for carrots but the main growing areas are limited by soil conditions. Carrots can only be grown successfully on a farm scale on deep sandy loams and black fen soils, mainly because it is easy to lift and clean the roots. Stony and shallow soils produce badly shaped roots which may be unsaleable.

Seed-bed: should be fine, firm, clean and level (as for sugar-beet). If there is a pan in the soil it must be broken by sub soiling.

Varieties. There are many good varieties which are grouped by the shape of root as *long, stump-rooted* and *intermediate.* The latter are the most common type.

Sowing. The seed, which usually has the bristles machined off it, may be sown shallow ($\frac{1}{2}$–1 in. deep) in:

(a) wide rows (18–20 in.)—weeds controlled by inter-row cultivations.

(b) narrow rows (6–8 in.) or in beds (3–4$\frac{1}{2}$ ft wide)—weeds controlled by chemicals.

The yield from (b) is very much greater due to the high plant population per acre.

Seed rate. Up to 4 lb/acre is sown where the crop is singled. This is not a common practice now when it is more usual to sow about 1–1$\frac{1}{2}$ lb/acre with a precision drill and leave all plants to mature.

F

Time of sowing: main crops—April, but varies from late February to March.

Manuring. F.Y.M. can be beneficial on sandy soils but it must be well rotted and ploughed in deeply in the autumn. The fertilizers used on average fertility soils without F.Y.M. should contain about 45 units N, 80 units P_2O_5 and 100 units K_2O. Three hundredweight per acre of salt may be applied several weeks before sowing and the potash reduced to 50 units.

Chemical weed control. This has greatly simplified carrot growing on many farms. Contact chemicals can be used to kill seedling weeds before the crop emerges (as in sugar-beet, see p. 216), or, vaporizing and some mineral oils can be used when the carrots are in the seedling stage to kill a wide range of weeds. Pre-emergent chemicals (e.g. chlorpropham) also give good results on some soils.

Harvesting. This usually starts in October and may continue well into the winter in areas where severe frost is not likely to cause damage. The crop is either lifted by hand or by various types of modified root harvesters.

Storage. Usually in small clamps with the soil in direct contact with the roots to help keep them fresh looking. Some are now stored indoors. For many markets it is now necessary to wash the carrots (usually by machines) before sale. They are often sold in net bags.

Seed Production

Crops grown for seed are usually inspected and certified by inspectors working under the guidance of the N.I.A.B. for most varieties of grasses, clovers, cereals and vegetable seeds; by Ministry of Agriculture Officials for potatoes; and by seed growers associations for local strains of grasses, clovers, etc.

Seed crops must be true to type and variety and as free as possible from seed borne diseases. The harvested seed must be clean, (free from weed seeds and rubbish), plump and not spoiled by bad weather; it must also have good germination (e.g. 90% or over for cereals).

Crops such as cereals, beans and peas are grown like ordinary grain crops but special precautions have to be taken to ensure that the seed crops are not contaminated in any way, e.g. by plants produced by seeds shed by a previous crop. Also, special precautions must be taken to control weeds; and at harvest, seed crops should be given priority. Drying must be done very carefully and all machinery must be thoroughly cleaned to avoid contamination with other seeds.

Potatoes for seed are grown in areas which have very few aphids so that the spread of *virus* diseases can be controlled. Such areas are found in the hilly parts of England and Wales, Scotland and Northern Ireland. The soil growing seed potatoes should not have grown potatoes during the previous 3 years (5 years in Scotland) and should be free of eelworms. The haulms are usually destroyed when most of the tubers are still fairly small, i.e. seed size (2–3 oz).

Grasses. With the exception of Italian ryegrasses, most other grasses can be harvested for seed for 2 or more years in succession. The land must be free of grass weeds—especially those with seeds which cannot be separated from the seed crop. Some are usually grown in rows (e.g. cocksfoot) and some broadcast (e.g. perennial ryegrass). White clover is sometimes sown with the grasses to improve the value of the sward for grazing during part of the year. The grass crops are best harvested with a binder, stooked and threshed when dry. Many crops are windrowed and then combined when reasonably dry.

Clovers. Seed is usually broadcast and undersown in a cereal crop. The red clovers are usually harvested once (in the following year) after taking a silage cut. Late flowering red may be left to produce a second seed crop. The simplest method of harvesting (usually in September) is to destroy most of the leafy growth with a contact chemical (e.g. DNBP, Diquat, PCP, or sulphuric acid) and then combine direct.

White clover is often sown with perennial ryegrass or meadow fescue. Successful harvesting is very dependent on good weather. In a bad season it may pay to collect the crop with a forage harvester and dry it carefully on a grass drier before threshing.

Sugar-beet, mangolds, fodder beet. These biennial plants produce seed in the year following sowing. Most of the seed is grown in special zoned areas (to avoid cross-fertilization) in the eastern counties. Young plants (stecklings) are grown in narrow rows from seed sown about July. It is desirable that the stecklings should be produced well away from the main sugar-beet areas (e.g. in the seed potato areas) to avoid carrying over virus yellows. They are transplanted in the autumn or spring and spaced about 2 ft apart in 2 ft rows. The crop is cut by hand, tied and stooked for drying— usually in August.

Kales, swedes, turnips, rapes, etc., are also biennial plants which produce seed in the year following sowing. Swedes and turnips sown in August and September are usually hardy enough to over-winter. Special precautions have to be taken to avoid cross-fertilization.

They are harvested in late summer—usually cut and tied with a binder. Detailed information on the production of seed from these and many other crops are given in N.I.A.B. seed production leaflets.

Suggestions for Classwork

1. If possible, visit a flour mill, a maltings, an oat processing mill; a sugar-beet factory and a seed cleaning plant.
2. Examine good and bad samples of all the cereal grains.
3. Visit growing crops of cereals, potatoes, roots, peas and beans, etc.
4. When visiting farms see and discuss the various methods used for handling and storing cereals and potatoes.
5. Make notes on the fertilizers used for the crops you visit.
6. Learn how to recognize the different cereals in the leafy stage.
7. Examine potato tubers stored in sprouting boxes and note the controlling effect of light on size of sprouts; see the colour differences between sprouts of different varieties.
8. Note that the haulms of different potato varieties vary in many ways—this is the only sure method of recognizing potato varieties.

9. Visit growing crops of peas and discuss how they are grown and harvested and the problems involved (e.g. damage by pigeons).
10. Visit sugar-beet crops at singling and harvesting times and discuss the problems involved.
11. Examine the different types of sugar-beet seed.

CHAPTER 5

GRASSLAND

GRASS is the most important crop in this country. About two-thirds of all the farmland is grass, although it is only about one-third in the drier, sunny, eastern areas. Moreover, it is well to remember that grass is a crop, not something which just grows in a field!

Types of Grassland

In the British Isles grassland can be broadly divided into three groups:

1. ROUGH MOUNTAIN AND HILL GRAZINGS

The plants making up this type of grassland are not of great value. They mainly consist of fescues, bents, nardus and molinia grasses, as well as cotton grass, heather and gorse. Only sheep and beef cattle rearing at very low stocking rates are possible. In some areas where the soil is extremely acid, reafforestation is being successfully carried out.

2. PERMANENT PASTURES

These are pastures which are never ploughed. This group covers a wide range, and the quality usually depends on the amount of perennial ryegrass present. A first-grade ryegrass permanent pasture contains over 30% of perennial ryegrass, and this is capable of maintaining a heavy stocking rate. The poorest permanent pastures are not much better than moorland.

3. LEYS

These are temporary swards which have been sown to grass for a limited period (1–4 years). In most cases they will produce more than permanent pastures due to the more productive plants which make up the sward. But this sward will not stand up so well to treading as the permanent pasture.

Plants making up the Ley

These can be grouped as follows:

Grasses
Legumes: (a) clovers
    (b) lucerne and sainfoin.
Herbs

The grasses and clovers can be divided into *varieties* and further divided into *strains*. There are often important growth differences between strains, for example, the hay strains are earlier to start growth in the spring, earlier to flower, have a taller habit of growth, more flowering stems, and are less leafy than the grazing strains of the same variety. Some varieties also have dual purpose strains which are suitable for either grazing or cutting.

Apart from these differences in strain, varieties can also be classified as:

Commercial strains

These are very early to start growth in the spring; they flower early, and have the typical upright habit of growth of the hay strain. They do not live long, but may be useful in short leys.

Pedigree strains

These are strains which have been carefully selected and bred, and which will do well in most parts of the country. The S strains from Aberystwyth, and the new continental strains are good examples. Most of them are not so early in the spring as the commercial strains, but they are leafier and they live longer, and will normally grow better in the autumn.

Grass Identification

Before it is possible to recognize plants in a grass field (see Table 9), it is necessary to know something about the parts which make up the plant.

VEGETATIVE (LEAFY) PARTS

Stem

(a) The *flowering stem* or *culm*. This grows erect and produces the flower. Most stems of annual grasses are culms.

(b) The *vegetative stem*. This does not produce a flower, and has not such an erect habit of growth as the culm. Perennial grasses have both flowering and vegetative stems.

Leaves. They are arranged on two alternate rows on the stem, and are attached to the stem at a node. Each leaf consists of two parts (see Fig. 38).

(a) The *sheath* which is attached to the stem.

(b) The *blade* which diverges from the stem.

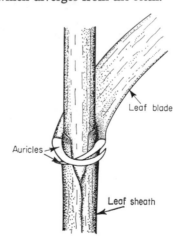

FIG. 38. Parts of the grass leaf.

The leaf sheath encloses the *buds* and *younger leaves*. Its edges may be *joined* (*entire*) or they may *overlap* each other (*split*) (see Fig. 39). If the leaves are *rolled* in the leaf sheath, the *shoots* will be *round* (see Fig. 40) but when *folded* the *shoots* will be *flattened* (see Fig. 41).

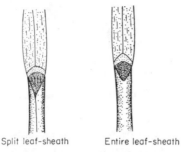

Split leaf-sheath   Entire leaf-sheath

FIG. 39. Parts of the grass leaf.

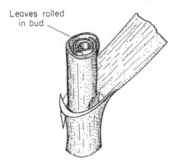

Leaves rolled
in bud

FIG. 40. Parts of the grass leaf.

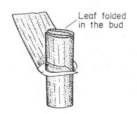

Leaf folded
in the bud

FIG. 41. Parts of the grass leaf.

At the junction between the leaf blade and leaf sheath is the *ligule*. This is an outgrowth from the inner lining of the sheath (see Fig. 42).

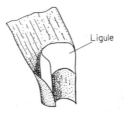

FIG. 42. Parts of the grass leaf.

The *auricles* may also be seen on some grasses where the blade joins the sheath. They are a pair of clawlike outgrowths. (see Fig. 38).

In some species, the leaf blade will show distinct veins when held against the light.

According to the variety, the underside of the leaf blade may be shiny or dull.

Other features of the leaves are more variable, and are not very reliable, and they can vary with age.

INFLORESCENCE—THE FLOWER HEAD OF THE GRASS

The inflorescence consists of a number of branches called *spikelets* which carry the flowers. There are two types of inflorescence:

(1) The *spike*—the spikelets are attached to the main stem without a stalk (see Fig. 43).

(2) The *panicle*—the spikelets are attached to the main stem with a stalk (see Fig. 44). In some grasses the spikelets are attached to the main stem with very short stalks to form a dense type of inflorescence termed *spike-like* (see Fig. 45).

The spikelet is normally made up of an *axis*, bearing at its base the *upper* and *lower glumes* (see Fig. 46). Most grasses have two glumes.

A spike
inflorescence

FIG. 43. Grass inflorescence.

A panicle
Inflorescence

FIG. 44. Grass inflorescence.

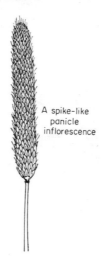

A spike-like
panicle
inflorescence

FIG. 45. Grass inflorescence.

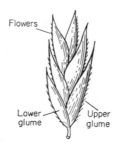

Flowers

Lower
glume

Upper
glume

FIG. 46. The spikelet.

Above the glumes, and arranged in the same way, are the *outer* and *inner pales*. In some species these pales may carry *awns* which are usually extensions from the pales (see Fig. 47).

Within the pales is the *flower*.

The flower consist of three parts (see Fig. 48).

(1) The male organs—*three stamens.*

(2) The female organ—the rounded *ovary* from which arise the feathery *stigmas*.

(3) A *pair* of *lodicules*—at the base of the ovary. They are indirectly concerned with the fertilization process, which is basically the same in all species of plants (see p. 23).

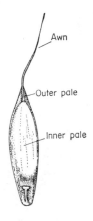

FIG. 47. The pales.

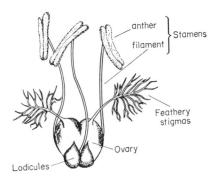

FIG. 48. The flower of the grass.

TABLE 9. HOW TO RECOGNIZE THE IMPORTANT GRASSES

	Short duration ryegrasses	Perennial ryegrass	Meadow fescue	Cocksfoot	Timothy
Leaf sheath	Definitely split. Pink at base. Rolled in shoot.	Split or entire. Pink at base. Folded in shoot.	Split. Pink at base. Rolled in shoot.	Entire. Folded in shoot.	Split. Pale at base. Rolled in shoot.
Blade	Broad. Margin smooth. Dark green.	Narrow. Margin smooth. Dark green.	Narrow. Margin rough. Lighter green.	Broad. Margin rough. Light green.	Broad. Margin smooth. Light green.
Lower side	Shiny.	Shiny.	Shiny.	Dull.	Dull.
Ligule	Blunt.	Short and blunt.	Small, blunt, greenish-white.	Long and transparent.	Prominent and membranous.
Auricles	Medium size and spreading.	Small, clasping the stem.	Small, narrow and spreading.	Absent.	Absent.
General	Veins indistinct when held to light. Not hairy.	Not hairy.	Veins appear as white lines when held to light. Not hairy.	Not hairy.	Base of shoots may be swollen. Not hairy.

Identification of the Legumes
See Table 10.

Leaves. With the exception of the first leaves (which may be simple) all leaves are compound. In some species the midrib is extended slightly to form a *mucronate* tip. Other features on the leaf may be *serrated* margins, presence or absence of marks, colour and hairyness (see Figs. 49 and 50). The leaves are arranged

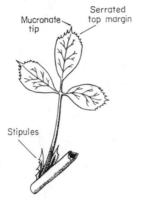

FIG. 49. Parts of the legume.

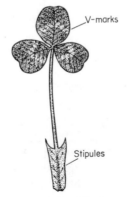

FIG. 50. Parts of the legume.

alternately on the stem, and they can consist of the *stalk* which bears two or more leaflets according to the species (see Fig. 51).

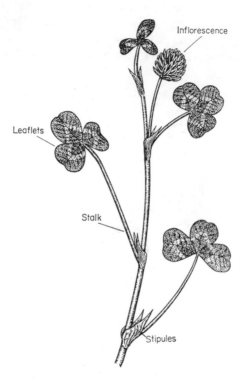

FIG. 51. Parts of the legume.

Stipules. These are attached to the base of the leaf stalk. They vary in shape and colour. (see Fig. 50).

Flower. The flowers are brightly coloured, and being arranged on a central axis form an indefinite type of inflorescence (see p. 24).

TABLE 10. How to Recognize the Important Legumes

	Leaves, etc.	Stipule	General	Species
Mucronate tip	Centre leaflet with prominent stalk. Leaflets serrated at tip.	Broad, serrated and sharply pointed.	May be hairy.	Lucerne
	6–12 pairs leaflets, plus a terminal one.	Thin, finely pointed.	Stems 1–2 ft high. Slightly hairy.	Sainfoin.
No mucronate tip	Trifoliate, dark green with white half moon markings on upper surface.	Membranous with greenish purple veins. Pointed.	Hairy	Red clover.
	Trifoliate, serrated edge with or without markings on upper surface.	Small and pointed.	Not hairy.	White clover.

Grasses

Over 150 different varieties of grasses can be found growing in this country, but only a few are of any importance to the farmer:

> The short duration ryegrasses—this class consists of varieties which fall into three main groups: Westerwolths ryegrass, Italian ryegrass, and H.1. short rotation ryegrass.
> Perennial ryegrass.
> Cocksfoot.
> Timothy.
> Meadow fescue.

The plant breeders are continually experimenting with other varieties of grasses, some of which may become important in the future, e.g. tall fescue.

SHORT DURATION RYEGRASSES (see Fig. 52)

Westerwolths

This is an annual and the quickest growing of all grasses. A good crop can often be obtained within 6-8 weeks of sowing.

Italian ryegrass.

This is short-lived; very quick to establish; produces tremendous bulk in its first year, and early bite for its 2 years. It does well under most conditions, but responds best to fertile soils and plenty of nitrogen. Although stemmy, it is palatable.

Irish is the best of many commercial strains, and the pedigree strain, S 22, is a leafy and more persistent type. The new Danish strains appear to be more winter-hardy.

H.1. short rotation ryegrass

This is very similar to S 22, but it should last longer, although it is not so winter-hardy.

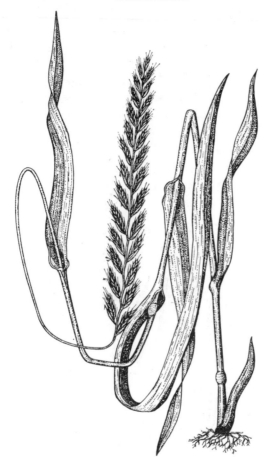

Fig. 52. Short duration ryegrass.

PERENNIAL RYEGRASS (see Fig. 53)

This forms the basis of the majority of long leys. The most important grass found in good permanent pastures. It is quick to establish, and yields well in the spring, early summer and autumn. It does best under fertile conditions, and responds well to nitrogen.

Examples of strains

Hay	Grazing	Dual-purpose
Barenza S24	Devon Eaver S 23 S 321	S 101

Fig. 53. Perennial ryegrass.

TETRAPLOID RYEGRASSES

These are new varieties. Their chromosome numbers in the cell nuclei have been doubled. These grasses are more palatable than the ordinary ryegrasses. The seeds are larger, which will mean a higher seedrate.

COCKSFOOT (see Fig. 54)

FIG. 54. Cocksfoot.

This is quick to establish, and is fairly early in the spring. It is the highest yielding of all grasses, but unless it is heavily stocked it will soon become coarse and unpalatable. It is one of the most deep-rooting of all grasses, and is therefore an excellent drought resister, and it does not need really fertile conditions.

Examples of strains

Hay	Grazing	Dual-purpose
Danish Tardus II S 37	S 345 S 143	S 26

TIMOTHY (see Fig. 55).

This is fairly quick to establish. It is not particularly early in the spring. It is less productive than the other commonly used grasses,

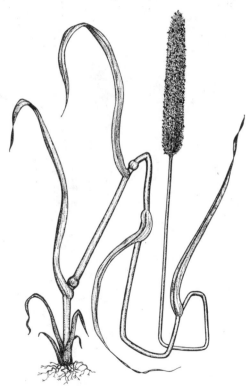

Fig. 55. Timothy.

but is very palatable. It is winter hardy, and does well under a wide range of conditions except on very light, dry soils.

Examples of strains

Hay	Grazing	Dual-purpose
Vanadis S 352 S 51	Sceempter S 50	S 48

FIG. 56. Meadow fescue.

MEADOW FESCUE (see Fig. 56)

This is rather slow to establish, but once established it is very productive. It is fairly early in the spring. It does very well when sown in conjunction with timothy.

Examples of strains

Hay	Grazing
Trifolium II S 215	S 53

Other Grasses

TALL FESCUE

Once it is well established, the strain S 170 is extremely useful for early grass in the spring, and being very hardy it can also be grazed in the winter.

RED FESCUE AND SHEEP'S FESCUE

Both are small plants which are only suitable for poor upland and marginal soils. They are more productive under these conditions than the better known grasses.

ROUGH AND SMOOTH STALKED MEADOW GRASS, AND CRESTED DOG'S TAIL

These used to be included in seeds mixtures. They are not, however, very productive, and are too expensive to consider these days.

WEED GRASSES

The majority of grasses naturally growing in this country are of little value. But some of them are extremely persistant and are able to grow under very poor conditions where the more valuable grasses would not thrive. However, their production is always low, they are usually unpalatable, and under most conditions they can be considered as weeds.

Well known examples of weed grasses are:

The bents. They are very unproductive and unpalatable and are found in poor permanent pastures.

Brome grasses. They are found in arable fields and also in short leys. There are many species, and none are of any value.

Yorkshire fog. This is extremely unpalatable except when very young. It is prevalent under acid conditions, although it can be found growing almost anywhere. It is sometimes used in reclaiming hill pastures.

Clovers

Clovers are essential plants for the longer ley and permanent pasture. In the short ley they are still used for hay and silage, although there is an increasing tendency not to include them in ryegrass mixtures intended chiefly for grazing. Apart from their ability to fix nitrogen from the atmosphere, clovers are also useful in that, especially in the longer ley, they act as "bottom plants". With their creeping habit of growth they knit the sward together and help to keep out weeds. Although the majority of clovers are palatable with a high feeding value, they are not so productive as the grasses, and they must not be allowed to dominate the sward at the expense of the grasses. The clovers of agricultural importance are the red and white clovers.

RED CLOVERS (see Fig. 57)

These are short lived. They are included in short leys and sometimes in long leys to improve bulk in the early years. Although used more for conservation, some of the more persistent improved strains are useful for grazing. There are two types.

FIG. 57. Red clover.

Broad red clovers

Dorset marl grass clover is one of the best of many local strains. It will last 2 years. S 151 is an improvement on other strains, but later to start growth in the spring.

Late flowering red clovers

These strains last longer than the broad red clovers. Under good conditions they persist for at least 3 years. They also stand up to grazing better than the other red clovers. S 123 can persist up to 4 years.

WHITE CLOVERS (see Fig. 58)

These should be regarded as the foundation of the grazing ley. They are not so productive as the red clovers, but are more persistant. There are two types.

FIG. 58. White clover.

Large white clovers

These are extremely useful in leys of up to 4 years and are very quick to establish. S 100 is the best known strain, and New Zealand white clover is very similar.

Wild white clovers

These are the most essential of all plants in the long ley. They are rather slow to establish, but can become very dominant. Kent wild white clover is a good local strain, and S 184 is another very productive and creeping type.

Other Legumes

LUCERNE (see Fig. 59)

This is a very productive legume. It is usually grown for conservation, but it is fairly useful for grazing. It is best to grow lucerne with a companion grass such as timothy or cocksfoot. This makes it easier to establish, and more palatable for grazing. Also silage and hay can be more easily made from a mixture rather than from lucerne alone. Lucerne is very deep rooting, and is therefore useful under dry soils, although it can be grown successfully under

FIG. 59. Lucerne.

a wide range of soil and climatic conditions. There are many varieties of lucerne, and in this country they can be grouped into *early* and *mid-season* types (see N.I.A.B. leaflet).

SAINFOIN (see Fig. 60)

FIG. 60. Sainfoin.

As regards its economic use, sainfoin is very similar to lucerne although it is not so productive. It has not been very popular in the past, due to difficulties in establishment (it does not compete very well with weeds), but sown with grasses such as cocksfoot, this problem has been overcome. For forage purposes especially it should be seriously considered for calcareous soils. Sainfoin hay is highly valued for horses, but it is difficult to make without losing leaf. There are two major types of sainfoin.

French or giant. This is heavy yielding, but short-lived.

Common or Old English. This lasts for several years, but is not so heavy yielding.

Herbs

These are deep-rooting plants which are generally beneficial to pastures. But to be of any value, they should be palatable, in no way harmful to stock, and they should not compete with other species in the sward. They have a high mineral content which may benefit the grazing animal.

Yarrow, chicory, rib grass and burnet (see Figs. 61–64) are the most useful of the many herbs which exist. They can be included in seeds mixture for a grazing type of long ley. They are not cheap, however, and as one or more of these herbs will usually get into the sward on its own accord, there does not seem much point in buying them in the first place.

FIG. 61. Yarrow.

FIG. 62. Chicory.

FIG. 63. Rib grass.

Fig. 64. Burnet.

Seeds Mixtures

Many farmers depend on reliable seeds firms to supply them with standard seeds mixtures, whilst others prefer to plan their own mixtures which the merchant will then make up for them.

The following points must be considered when deciding upon a seeds mixture.

THE PURPOSE OF THE LEY

Varieties and strains of herbage plants have different growth characteristics, and because of this the type of stock using the ley will influence the choice of seed. This is shown in Table 11.

TABLE 11.

Purpose	Varieties which should be used
For early grazing in the spring, i.e. early bite.	Mainly ryegrass or possibly tall fescue.
For an attempted even balance of production throughout the season.	Ryegrass and non-ryegrass.
For winter grazing cattle—foggage (provided conditions allow).	Cocksfoot and timothy.
For the grazing animal only (particularly sheep).	Strains of grasses which produce a closely knit sward.
For conservation only (silage and hay).	Strains of grasses which produce a tall habit of growth.

SOIL AND CLIMATIC CONDITIONS

Most strains of grasses and legumes will grow where there is a reasonable amount of rainfall, but in dry conditions deep-rooting and therefore drought resistant plants, such as cocksfoot, lucerne, and sainfoin are advisable. On heavy, wet soils there is no point in growing early grasses or planning for foggage grazing. Like the majority of crops, grasses and particularly legumes will not thrive where there is a lack of lime in the soil.

THE LENGTH OF THE LEY

Perennial ryegrass, cocksfoot, timothy and meadow fescue, being persistent, are suitable for long leys, whilst the less persistent and quick-growing early types, of which Italian ryegrass is an outstanding example, will make up the short ley.

G

COST OF THE MIXTURE

This will vary from season to season depending upon the previous year's seed harvest, the strain of plant used and the seed rate. It is false economy to buy unsuitable strains just because they are cheap. It is equally unwise to be persuaded to buy expensive and often unproved seed. Generally speaking, it will be found that varieties required for the short term ley are cheaper than those for the longer ley.

Tables 12–14 give examples of different seeds mixtures.

Some terms used in Grassland Management

Before discussing establishment, manuring and general management of leys it is important to understand what is meant by the following expressions:

> *Seeding year:* the year in which the seeds mixture is sown.
> *First harvest year:* the first year after the seeding year, and thus the second and third, etc., harvest years.
> *Undersowing:* sowing the seeds mixture with another crop (a cover crop). It is usually a cereal crop.
> *Direct sowing or seeding:* sowing on bare ground without a cover crop.

Direct re-seeding strictly means sowing without a cover crop, and putting the field straight back to grass, the previous crop having been grass. Very often it is used in the same way as direct sowing.

Making a New Ley

A case can be made for sowing the seeds either in the spring or late summer/early autumn period.

SPRING SOWING

If direct sowing without a cover crop, the maiden seeds can give valuable production in the summer. Establishment can be enhanced by stock being able to graze the developing sward within a few

TABLE 12. 1-YEAR LEYS (AMOUNTS IN LB/ACRE)

	Westerwolths	Commercial I.R.G.	Broad red clover	Late flowering red clover	Total	
A	25–30				25–30	Not suitable for undersowing; extremely quick to establish; will produce two good cuts or grazings, especially if the first one is taken before the seeds are set.
B		20–40			20–40	The lower seed rate is used in the wetter parts of the country. Stemmy but palatable. Chiefly used for grazing.
C		15 comm. 15 S.22			30	Becoming quite popular; for general use, although chiefly for grazing.
D		16	6		22	When undersown will give autumn grazing. In the following year two good crops, usually, but not always, for conservation.
E		16	4	3	23	Very similar to mixture D—but will give better after-math grazing because of the inclusion of the L.F.R.C.

In the examples given ryegrass is the only variety of grass used. The emphasis must be on quick establishment with good production from an early stage, and with an ability to respond well to nitrogen. As persistency is not important, the short rotation ryegrasses will amply fulfill these requirements, provided that management is correct.

TABLE 13. 2-4-YEAR LEYS (AMOUNTS IN LB/ACRE)

	H 1 ryegrass	S 22 I.R.G.	Perennial ryegrass S 24	Cocksfoot S 37	Timothy S 48	Meadow fescue S 53	Broad red clover S 151	Late flowering red clover S 123	White clover S 100 or N.Z.W.C.	Total	
A	4 or	4	12				2	3	1	22	This mixture should give early bite, an extremely useful hay or silage crop and good aftermath grazing, but plenty of nitrogen will be needed for maximum production. If S 24 is replaced by S 101 the ley should last 4 years.
B	20						2			22	A mixture which should quite easily last 3 years, but if growing conditions are not ideal replace 10 lb of H 1 ryegrass with 10 lb S 23. This is an easy ley to manage, and can be extremely productive when liberally fed with nitrogen.
C	10	10	10							30	A very productive ley. With no clover to depress, up to 300 units of nitrogen can be economically applied in the season.
D					8	10			2	20	More of a grazing mixture. Not early in the spring, but should give even production throughout the season with good late grazing. This mixture would not do so well on lighter soils, but if, say, 5 lb S 143 cocksfoot were added it would be more productive under those conditions.
E		4		14				3	1	22	For really poor soil types this mixture would be suitable for general purpose use.

TABLE 14. LONG LEYS (AMOUNTS IN LB/ACRE)

	Perennial ryegrass	Cocksfoot	Timothy S 48	Meadow fescue S 215	Late flowering red S 123 clover	White clover S 100 or N.Z.W.C.	Wild white clover S 184	Total	
A	20 S 23					2	½	22½	For general purpose use. A very productive and hard-wearing ley.
B			8	10		2	½	20½	For general purpose use. This ley will tie in well with the previous ryegrass mixture, and by managing the two leys together it should be possible to get fairly even production throughout the season.
C		5 S 26 5 S 37 5 S 143				2	½	17½	This mixture could be managed in a similar way as B, but is suited to the lighter, poorer soils.
D	13 S 101	7 S 26	4		3	1	½	28½	This is the famous Cockle Park type general purpose mixture. It is meant to give even production throughout the whole season, but eventually, depending upon the soil type and management, it will tend to become either ryegrass or cocksfoot dominant.

It will be noted that wild white clover is included in these mixtures. After about 3 years it should have established itself sufficiently well to fill in the bottom of the ley and give a nice well-knit sward. Only a small amount is needed, otherwise it will tend to dominate the whole sward at the expense of the more productive grasses.

weeks of sowing. This is not possible to the same extent with autumn sowing. A limiting factor with spring sowing may be moisture, and in the drier districts, the seeds should be sown at the beginning of March if possible. The plant should thus establish itself sufficiently well to withstand a probable dry period in late spring. Of course, undersowing in corn (which is only possible in the spring) does mean that the fullest possible use is being made of the field, although with the slower growing grasses, establishment is usually not so good.

LATE SUMMER/EARLY AUTUMN SOWING

There is usually some rain at this time; heavy dews have started again, and the soil is warm. But with clovers in the seeds mixture earlier sowing may have to be carried out so that the plants have developed a good tap root system before the onset of frosts. Earlier sowing is not always possible.

UNDERSOWING OR DIRECT SOWING

There are points for and against either of the practices, but in general undersowing is more popular. However, where conditions are not so good, and where extra grass is required in the summer, direct sowing is preferable. But with short leys, undersowing is more normally carried out.

Green crops as cover crops are excellent, e.g.,

(1) Rape sown at 4–6 lb/acre with the seeds mixture, and grazed off in 6–10 weeks.
(2) Oats or barley sown at 56 lb/acre with the seeds mixture.
(3) Oats and vetches as arable silage which is cut green at the end of May.

Sowing the Crop

DIRECT SOWING

Reference has already been made to the cultivations necessary for preparing the right sort of seed-bed for the seeds (see p. 77).

But it must be re-emphasized that grass and clover seeds are small, and therefore they must be sown shallow, and that therefore a fine and firm seed-bed is necessary.

With ample moisture the seed can be broadcast. This should be on a ribbed-rolled surface, so that the seeds tend to fall into the small furrows made by the roller. Most fertilizer distributors can be used for broadcasting, or for smaller acreages, the shandy barrow is still very useful.

In the drier areas, and on lighter soils, drilling is safer. The seed is then in much closer contact with the soil. The 4 in. coulter spacing of the ordinary grass drill should give a satisfactory cover of seeds, but if using the corn drill with 7 in. spacing, the seeds should be cross-drilled. After either broadcasting or drilling, except on the wetter seed-beds (when the seeds harrow will be used), rolling will complete the whole operation. If necessary, 3 cwt of a general compound fertilizer can either be broadcast and worked in during the final seed-bed preparations, or, depending on the drill used, it can be applied with the seed.

UNDERSOWING

If the cover crop is *autumn sown*, it will be usually wheat or oats. Harrowing of the ground will be necessary, and then the seed should preferably be drilled across the corn drills followed by the light harrows. Alternatively, the seed can be broadcast and harrowed in, but this is not so satisfactory.

With *spring sown* cover crop the cereal is sown first and can be immediately followed by the seeds mixture drilled or broadcast. This is desirable with slow establishing mixtures but with vigorous species e.g. Italian ryegrass and red clover it may be preferable to broadcast the seed after the cereal is established.

Manuring of Grassland

Grass, like all crops, needs plant food for its establishment, maintenance and production. *Nitrogen* is essential for maximum production from the ley. How much to apply will depend, to a certain extent, on the composition of the sward. Too much nitrogen, especially if the resulting sward is not properly utilized can lead to a definite checking of the clovers. With a straight grass mixture (especially ryegrass) up to 300 units of nitrogen can economically be applied, provided other plant foods are in adequate supply.

It would be very unwise to apply all the nitrogen needed by the ley for the year in one application. Most of it would be wasted. It should be applied "little and often" from early February to October if necessary, depending upon the swards. It is important to use nitrogen, not only during natural periods of growth, i.e. spring and early autumn, but also to try and force production at other times of the season. This refers to ordinary fertilizers (see also p. 89).

Phosphate and *potash* will both help in the establishment of the sward, and on most soils they are important in helping to maintain the general vigour and well-being of the ley. There is no doubt that the response to nitrogen by the grass crop is far greater if there is an adequate supply of phosphate and potash present. These plant foods should be applied in the autumn whenever possible, at about 80 units each per acre.

The Management of a Young Ley

A DIRECT-SOWN LONG LEY IN ITS SEEDING YEAR—SOWN IN THE SPRING

The sward should be grazed 6–10 weeks after sowing, depending upon weather conditions which naturally affect growth. This early grazing helps to consolidate the developing sward, and encourages the plant to tiller out. It should not be too hard, but equally it is important not to undergraze. The sward should then be rested, and followed by periodic grazings throughout the season.

It is unwise to cut the ley in its seeding year. Plants which are allowed to grow too tall before being cropped never develop very strongly. The essential tillering is not encouraged to the same extent, and the sward is left "very open" into which weeds may soon gain a foothold.

If grazing is not possible, the plants should be topped before they grow too tall.

A DIRECT-SOWN LEY—SOWN IN THE LATE SUMMER

This should either be grazed or topped in the autumn.

AN UNDERSOWN LEY

This should either be grazed or topped in the autumn. If the seeds look "thin" after the corn has been harvested, 20 units of nitrogen will help to stimulate growth.

Management of the Established Ley

Basically only *ryegrass* and *non-ryegrass* leys need be considered. General purpose mixtures eventually become either ryegrass or cocksfoot (non-ryegrass) dominant, depending upon soil type and management.

ALTERNATING SWARDS

This should be the basis of grassland management. Simple mixtures, managed side by side. The farmer should have on his farm ryegrass and non-ryegrass mixtures. They grow at different times, and thus it is possible, with suitable fertilizer treatment, to obtain a fairly uniform supply of grass throughout the growing period. Of course, this will not always happen. The actual pattern of production in any one year is very much dependent on the season. But this type of management should be attempted. The grass year should commence in the autumn, when the crop is exhausted after its season's production; it is then that it needs replenishment in order to build up its reserves again for the next year.

Tables 15 and 16 show ways of managing grassland. Naturally, there will have to be modifications according to season, growth and type of stock available. The management chiefly refers to the dairy cow, although some intensive beef grazing system can also apply. (Mention will be made of sheep grazing on p. 193).

TABLE 15. MANAGEMENT OF LONG LEYS

		Jan.	Feb.	Mar.	April	May	June	July	Aug.	Sept.	Oct.	Nov.	Dec.
Production	Ryegrass leys												
	Non-ryegrass leys												
Manuring and	Ryegrass leys		Apply 60 units N to sheltered early fields for early bite.	(1) (2) (3) (4) (5) (6)	(1) Early bite taken. (2) 40 units N applied after grazing. (3) Graze at intervals throughout summer period; any surplus taken for conservation. (4) Additional Nitrogen applied at 40 units a time after every crop or every other crop has been taken, depending on the season. (5) Avoid, if possible, cropping in July and August. (6) Reasonably heavy grazing can be continued fairly late in the year to check the grasses and encourage the clovers.						(1) Apply 80 units each of P_2O_5 and K_2O; 6 cwt of slag can replace the phosphate every 4 yrs. Do not graze stock after slag application until it is well washed in. (2) For early bite, shut the field up after fertilizer application. (3) Lime, if required.		
Management and	Non-ryegrass leys		Foggage taken from well-drained dry fields.	(1) (2) (3) (4)	(1) 40–60 units N applied. (2) Graze at intervals throughout summer period, if possible taking any surplus for conservation. (3) Additional Nitrogen applied at 30 units a time, after every crop or every other crop has been taken, depending on the season. (4) Particular attention should be paid to getting production in July or August, when normally ryegrass leys will not be growing well.					(1) Apply 30 units N, and 80 units each of P_2O_5 and K_2O. Slag at 6 cwt every 4 yrs. to replace the phosphate. (2) If necessary, shut the ley up after fertilizer application for foggage grazing late in the winter (if conditions permit). (3) Lime, if required.			

This type of programme on these special purpose leys can be followed every year, modifying it according to season, state of the sward and the needs of the stock. In some years grazing should not be so intensive, and more conservation can be taken, and grazing should be finished earlier. All this will tend to check the clovers, and encourage the grasses. Thus it is a fairly easy matter to maintain a reasonably correct balance between the clovers and the grasses. Too much clover in the sward should be avoided, although too little clover will lead to an unproductive ley.

TABLE 16. MANAGEMENT OF SHORT LEYS

	Seeding year	First year	Second year	
1 year ley	After the cover crop has been removed, 30 units N can be applied to give useful grazing in September and October. Apply 40 units each of P_2O_5 and K_2O after this grazing.	If early bite is required, 60 units N applied in February. Following early bite, 60 units N can be applied for conservation, followed by a further 60 units N for a second cut or graze.		Lime should not be necessary. If possible, the arable break in the rotation should receive the lime. Rolling will probably be necessary in early spring as the leys are usually cut, and it is wise to press the stones down firmly.
2 year ley	As for the 1-year ley.	As for the 1-year ley, with the addition of 40 units each of P_2O_5 and K_2O in the autumn.	As for the previous year, except that the autumn application of P_2O_5 and K_2O will not be needed.	

Grazing by Stock

All stock do not graze in the same way. Some are much better grazers than others. The most efficient are store cattle, followed by dairy cows and fattening cattle, sheep and young cattle. Horses are notoriously bad grazers!

Mixed stocking is ideal. In this way fairly good utilization of the sward is achieved because what is not eaten by one class of stock will probably be consumed by other classes of stock. Mixed stocking is not always possible. But what should be done is to see that the most profitable stock get the best. This usually means the dairy cow or fattening beast, and at certain times of the year, the sheep flock.

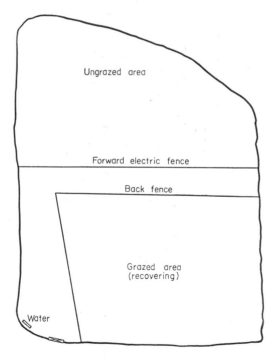

FIG. 65. Strip grazing.

INTENSIVE GRAZING

The introduction of the electric fence brought about one of the greatest revolutions in grassland farming. By its use controlled grazing is possible.

There are two methods of controlled grazing:

(1) *Strip grazing* (see Fig. 65). This is particularly suitable for the dairy cow, whereby the animal is allowed access to a limited area of fresh crop either twice daily, daily, or longer intervals. This is certainly the most efficient form of grazing. If no other stock are following on behind the cows, the back fence should be used, whereby the area once grazed is almost immediately fenced off. This is to protect the recovering sward from constantly being

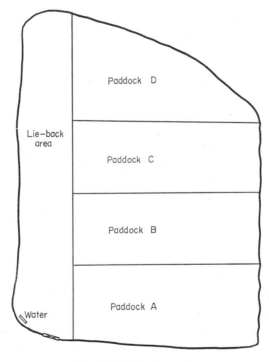

FIG. 66. Paddock grazing.

nibbled over. Without the back fence the recovery rate is very much slower.

(2) *Paddock grazing* (see Fig. 66). With this method of grazing, the field is divided into paddocks which are intensively grazed in turn by stock. This is a less intensive form of grazing compared with strip grazing, but the chore of continually having to move the electric fence is avoided.

Stocking Rates

FOR CONTROLLED GRAZING OF DAIRY COWS OR FATTENING BEASTS

Stocking rates must depend on the amount of grass available, and obviously at certain times of the year it can be very much higher than at other times.

When the sward is growing well, and at about 6–8 in. high, *fifty cows* will need about *one acre per day* of fresh grass. Any surplus grass should, if possible, be cut for hay or silage, and naturally adjustments will have to be made when the crop is not so productive. Much depends on the actual breed and temperament of the animals, as well as on the growth of the grass. The yard-stick must be the production and condition of the stock, coupled as far as possible with the condition of the sward, although too much emphasis should not be placed on this second point. Given a reasonable rest period, a good ley will soon recover, but the mower may have to be used to top-over the uneven effects of grazing.

The rationing of grassland is an art, but it can be acquired by an observant stockman.

FOLLOWING STOCK

Followers can be fitted in behind these stock to graze extensively, although grazing management is often easier when it is not complicated by following stock. It is an increasing practice to keep some leys exclusively for intensive milk or meat production, and other pastures (sometimes permanent pastures) are kept for the followers. Calves should be grazed on new swards.

Fattening Cattle Under Extensive Grass Management Conditions

Although cattle can be fattened successfully on leys under the intensive conditions described, the majority of farmers fattening beasts prefer to do so more extensively. The management is entirely different. Very often the stock are turned into the field at the beginning of the grazing season, and are kept there all the time. For finishing off of strong stores on grass, a stocking rate of one bullock per acre is usual, and this animal should be able to put on a liveweight increase of 2 cwt in the season May till August.

Good permanent pastures are generally preferred by the fattener. There is something in a permanent pasture (and it is hard to explain what it is!) which finishes off a beast that much better compared with most leys.

With permanent pasture, particularly, the farmer will usually know its capabilities throughout the season. He will be able to adjust the stocking according to previous experience, and also, of course, by the appearance of the stock. Rate of growth will, to a certain extent, depend upon the type of season.

Grazing with Sheep

For quite a large part of the year the grass sheep flock should be regarded as a scavenger flock. There is no reason to treat them otherwise.

It is impossible to give any hard and fast rules on the rates of stocking. The grass will obviously not be at its best, as other stock would have already been over it. The sheep are simply clearing up. Therefore the condition of the stock must be watched and stocking rates adjusted accordingly. But do not overgraze the pasture with sheep.

Better grass is needed for ewes being flushed, and for ewes and lambs for fat lamb production.

ROTATIONAL CREEP-GRAZING

Systems of rotational creep-grazing have recently been developed, whereby the lambs have access to unlimited supplies of fresh grass without competition from the ewes. Very impressive performances have been recorded of liveweight gains of the lambs, and coupled with the heavy stocking rates possible (up to eight ewes and their lambs to the acre) this type of intensive management of sheep on leys may be worth considering. More fencing is needed, and more labour is involved at the beginning of the season to put up the paddocks and creeps.

Some farmers favour less intensive systems of sheep grazing, such as set stocking in one field, or rotational set stocking whereby two or three fields are used in turn throughout the season by the flock.

The Improvement of Pastures

Poor permanent pasture can be recognized by a mat of old decaying vegetation at the bottom of the sward. This is usually the result of poor management over a long period, such as bad grazing and not enough fertilizer. The better plants are choked out, and inferior grasses such as the bents are encouraged. The cheapest, simplest and quickest way of improving an old pasture is to plough it up and direct re-seed it. This is not always possible, and so the mat must be destroyed in other ways. Until recently, pasture improvement (other than ploughing) was a slow process involving drastic harrowing of the sward to pull out old vegetation, followed by liming and fertilizers, particularly phosphate, to encourage the better grasses and clovers. If necessary, a seeds mixture could be broadcast on the field.

The use of stock to bite down the new growth and encourage tillering will bring about a gradual improvement of the sward. But it is only gradual, usually taking a number of years to upgrade the pasture. Various chemicals are now available to help destroy the mat more quickly, and, if necessary, a sod seeder can be used to plant the seeds into the soil. A more rapid improvement of the sward will follow. Some chemicals will completely kill the old sward, and the field can be re-seeded to grass without any cultural operations (see page 219).

Haymaking

Too much poor quality hay is made in this country. Apart from the wet weather, poor quality herbage and inefficient methods of making are mainly responsible. Although crops such as lucerne, sainfoin and cereal/pulse mixtures can be used for hay, the cheapest and generally most satisfactory crop for hay is grass which should be cut at the flower emergence stage.

The critical period for hay occurs when the crop is partly dried in the field, and therefore there is a *golden rule for haymaking*. No more hay should be ready for picking up in one day than can be dealt with by the equipment and staff. If the cutting outstrips the drying and collection, the hazards of weather damage are greatly increased. Thus, if the baler can only deal with, say, fifteen acres in the day, then cutting should be in fifteen acre lots.

The object in haymaking should be to dry the crop as rapidly as possible without too much exposure to sun and the least possible movement after the crop is partially dry. Consequently, there are only two methods of making hay worth considering:

(a) The quick haymaking method whereby the crop is baled in the quickest possible time consistent with its safety.

(b) Barn drying of hay.

QUICK HAYMAKING

With this method, there are three stages in the making of hay.

(1) Fresh Crop 75–80% m.c.

Curing in the field

(2) 25% m.c.

Drying in the bale in the field

(3) 20–22% m.c.

Drying in the stack

Hay—safe for storage 18% m.c.

(1) *Curing in the field.* The crop should be cut when it is dry and when the weather appears to be set fine. The local meteorological office will give a weather forecast for 2–3 days ahead. If possible the

headlands of the field should be cut earlier for silage. Hay on the headland usually takes longer to dry out than the rest of the field. As soon as the crop has been cut, it should be moved unless the weather has become unsettled. Usually the tedder, but sometimes the turner, is used to start the drying. As soon as the top is drier than the bottom of the broken swath, it should be turned again. This may mean moving the crop with the tedder two or three times the first day. If the weather looks a little unsettled, it will be advisable to row the crop up in the evening. It will take far less damage in a row than when scattered all over the field. The next morning, as soon as the dew is off the ground, the rows should be opened out if necessary, and the crop again moved as on the previous day. But as it gets drier it should be handled far more gently, using only the turner.

It may be necessary to row the crop at night, and the next morning when the dew is gone it should be turned, maybe twice, and then it may possibly be ready for baling. But this does depend on the weather, the size and type of crop, and because of these factors it may be *at least* another day before the hay is fit to bale.

Only the general principles of field curing have been given. Other implements, such as the flail mower crimper or forage-harvester, can also be used to quicken up the process of drying.

Although it is convenient to talk in terms of moisture content in connection with stages of drying, at present there is no reliable moisture meter to test the moisture content of the crop in the field. It is a question of experience in deciding when the hay is fit to bale. As a guide, when only a little sap is expelled from the nodes, and the stems break quite easily, baling can commence. The moisture content will be approximately 25–27%.

(2) *Drying in the bale.* As the hay has been baled with a high moisture content drying should continue in the bale. With average weather the ram-type bale, if left in heaps, will dry out quite considerably in 2–3 days without any protection, even if they have not been stooked. Unless the hay is very dry when baled, it is a risk to cart the bales in at once. Heating and subsequent moulding in the stack will generally take place. Round bales are virtually

weatherproof, and they may be left to dry slowly in the field for some weeks.

(3) *Drying in the stack.* There are various ways in which the bales can be picked up from the field prior to stacking.

The stack is usually built under a Dutch barn. With any type of stack a good level bottom is necessary, one formed of substantial rough timbers is ideal to keep the first layer of bales well clear of the ground.

The stack walls must be built carefully and firmly. Within the walls, the bales should be stacked leaving air spaces between them. They should not be squeezed in. There are two reasons for this:

(a) The moisture content at stacking will generally be about 22%. It will eventually drop to about 16%. This moisture must be allowed to escape.

(b) As the bales are not very dense, they will, in the lower layers of the stack, tend to be squeezed out by the weight of the bales above. Therefore, cavities between the bales will reduce the tendency of the walls to "belly out".

A good layer of straw should be put on top of the stack to soak up the escaping moisture. This will help to prevent the top layers of bales from going mouldy.

THE BARN DRYING OF HAY

This is a process whereby partially dried herbage is dried sufficiently for storage by having heated or unheated air passed through it. The great advantage of barn drying is that the crop is only partially dried before being carried in from the field, thus compared with most other methods it is left for a shorter time to the hazards of the weather. Bleaching by the sun and leaf-shatter will be far less. It should therefore be a much leafier, more palatable and more nutritious product.

There are basically two methods of drying:

(1) The storage drier
(2) The batch drier, and a modification of the batch drier whereby the hay is dried in the field. This is known as tunnel drying.

The principle with both systems of drying is that the bales are placed on a flat, evenly ventilated floor through which air is forced by a fan. Under average conditions about one day's curing in the field is necessary to get the crop half dried. It is then baled and placed in the drier.

With the storage drier. Four to five layers are dried at the start, using cold air only, and after 2–3 days (depending on drying conditions) further layers of bales are added and dried to complete, eventually, the filling of the building (see Fig. 67). The bales remain in the barn until required.

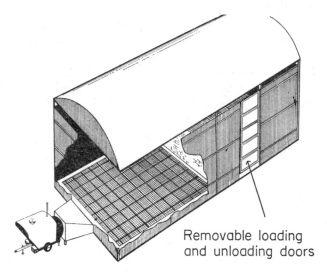

Removable loading and unloading doors

Fig. 67. Drying in the barn.

With the batch drier. Normally only about four layers of bales are dried at any one time. Heated air is usually required to complete drying of the batch within a certain time. The bales are then removed to make way for a further batch. This method of drying is largely being replaced by the storage drier or tunnel drying.

Tunnel drying. The bales (up to 1500) are built into a stack in the form of a tunnel blocked at one end. Some form of central support will be necessary for the tunnel which so constructed acts as a chamber into which the fan blows air, the only exit being through the bales themselves (see Fig. 68). Although this is generally not such an efficient method of drying the bales, no buildings are necessary, and drying usually takes place in the field.

FIG. 68. Tunnel drying.

Barn hay drying is not without its snags. It involves more labour than ordinary swath curing, and with the batch system especially this labour is needed at somewhat unpredictable times. It is also more expensive. But a very superior hay can be produced.

TRIPODING OF HAY

Although good quality hay can be made by curing the crop on wooden frameworks in the field, it is a very slow and laborious method.

Silage

Silage is produced by conserving green crops in a succulent state. The actual conservation process is known as ensilage and the container in which the material is placed is a silo. Good silage is a most valuable feeding stuff for both cattle and sheep.

CROPS FOR SILAGE

Grass is the most satisfactory crop for silage and if it is cut at about the pre-flowering stage it should provide good quantity with

H

reasonable quality. Lacerated or chopped grass ensiles more easily than long material.

Many other crops can be ensiled such as:

(a) *Lucerne*. Sometimes this crop produces rather poor silage, but with the new cold fermentation process this crop appears to be a better proposition.

(b) *Arable crops*. A mixture of oats and vetches, or maize, can yield very heavy crops for silage, but they are rather poor in protein and compared with grass are rather expensive crops to grow just for silage.

(c) *By-product silages*, e.g. that produced from sugar-beet tops and pea haulms, can be of high quality provided the material is ensiled clean.

Silos

The size of silos varies—about 50 ft³ equals 1 ton of made grass silage, or 1 ft³ equals 40 lb silage (this will vary according to the depth).

FIG. 69. Stack silo.

There are various types of silos.

(1) *Stack silos* (see Fig. 69). These are not commonly made these days. They have two major drawbacks in that (a) there can be excessive side wastage (no protecting sides), (b) tractor consolidation

is not possible which usually means that the silage in the upper part of the stack becomes over-heated. Within reason, the larger the stack silo the better as this should mean a smaller proportion of wastage.

(2) *Pit silos* (see Fig. 70). These are very satisfactory. They can be earth or concrete lined. There should be little wastage at the sides as the silage is not exposed to the air, and good overall tractor consolidation is possible. But they cannot be used under heavy soil conditions, and hauling the cut silage out during the winter is often difficult.

FIG. 70. Pit silo.

Dimensions: depth up to 10 ft (depends on the soil), width 16/20 ft, and length according to the amount of silage required.

(3) *Clamp silos*

(a) *The run-over clamp* (see Fig. 71). This is so made that the tractor and buckrake is run drawn right over it. Good consolidation is thus achieved, but wastage at the sides can be heavy.

FIG. 71. Run-over clamp.

(b) *The wedge-clamp* (see Fig. 72). This can be made very easily in conjunction with the buckrake. The tractor and buckrake back up the wedge, the sides and one end being kept vertical. There is good consolidation, but side wastage.

FIG. 72. Wedge clamp.

(c) *Walled clamp silos.* These cost more to build, but side wastage should be largely overcome with the protected sides.

Dimensions: For clamp silos the settled height should not be less than 6 ft, and the width up to 20 ft or more, with the length depending upon the amount of silage to be made.

(4) *Dutch barn silos* (see Fig. 73). These are the most satisfactory types of silos. The silage is protected all the time and a much drier silage is produced. These silos are, of course, expensive, but in addition they can be used for storage of hay and straw.

FIG. 73. Dutch barn silo.

(5) *Air-tight tower silos* (see Fig. 74). These are constructed of galvanized steel and are normally glass-lined or treated to make them air-tight and acid-resistant (see p. 207).

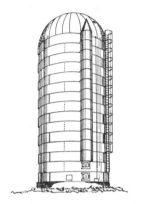

FIG. 74. Air-tight tower silo.

DRAINAGE OF SILOS

Unless the silo is well drained the bottom layers of silage will soon putrify. A simple drain is all that is necessary to get the effluent away. The simplest method is to have the silo floor sloping from one end to the other, with a cross drain at the lower end, although there are more expensive modifications.

Harvesting the Crop for Silage

The *forage-harvester* is the most commonly used machine for cutting and collecting the crop. It is used with high-sided trailers which collect the grass as it is blown from the "spout" of the harvester. Normally these trailers will dump the grass by the silo which is then filled with the buckrake.

The *buckrake*, as a means of collecting the crop from the field, is still worth considering when only a small quantity of silage is to be made, and where the distance of travel from field to silo is no more than a half-mile. The buckrake is much cheaper than the forage-harvester.

Silage Making

THE FERMENTATION PROCESS

In silage making this is essentially a matter of the breakdown of the carbohydrate. It takes place in two stages:

(1) *By respiration and development of heat.* When the plant is cut off from its roots, and is placed in a silo, respiration is continued by the cells taking in oxygen from the air in the ensiled crop, and carbon dioxide from the carbohydrate is given off. This respiration and breakdown of the carbohydrate brings about a rise in temperature. The more air there is present the more the respiration and breakdown of carbohydrate.

(2) *By bacterial action.* Eventually, as the supply of free air lessens, a different set of changes take place, whereby bacteria, which are always present on the green crop, act on the carbohydrate to produce organic acids. Two main acids can be produced by their respective bacteria, *lactic acid*, which is highly desirable, and *butyric acid* which is very undesirable.

Thus the stage is reached when the green crop is "pickled" in the acid; this, in fact, is silage, and what type of acid dominates depends upon the type of fermentation. This can be controlled to a large extent by the farmer himself.

As a result of different types of fermentation, three main types of silage can be produced as in Table 17.

HOT AND COLD SILAGE

There are two techniques which can be applied in making lactic acid silage:

(a) The so-called hot fermentation method.

(b) The cold fermentation method.

The difference between these two techniques is a matter of temperature.

TABLE 17. TYPES OF SILAGE

Silage	Sample	Feeding value	Reasons	Prevention
Overheated	Colour: brown to black. Smell: burnt sugar. Texture: dryish.	Although palatable, nutritionally is poor. Carbohydrates have been burnt up and protein digestibility considerably impaired by the high temperature.	Temperature remains at 120°F (49°C) or more, due to an appreciable amount of air present in the silo. This happens when stemmy and/or over-wilted material is insufficiently consolidated.	Do not let the crop get too mature before ensiling. When necessary fill the silo quickly and consolidate thoroughly. A stack silo should be built in an emergency.
Butyric acid	Colour: drab, olive green. Smell: unpleasant and rancid. Texture: slimy, soft tissues easily rubbed from fibres. Taste: not sharp, pH over 4·5.	Reasonably palatable and nutritionally quite good, but this depends on the stage of butyric acid fermentation. With very butyric silage, palatability will be poor and much of the protein will have been broken down by the spoiling bacteria. In extreme cases the silage may become toxic, especially to younger stock.	The butyric acid bacteria are allowed to dominate, conditions being unfavourable for the growth of the desirable bacteria, i.e. when young, leafy and unwilted crops with a high moisture content are put into the silo, and also when soil contaminated crops (butyric acid bacteria most commonly occur in the soil) are ensiled. The growth of the lactic acid bacteria is slow under these conditions, and therefore they do not produce sufficient acid to prevent the butyric acid bacteria from maintaining and increasing their presence.	Create unfavourable conditions for the butyric acid bacteria, i.e. encourage the lactic acid bacteria. Ensile dry, and possibly wilted crops, and, if necessary (with a young sappy crop), use some form of additive. Create an intense acid medium as quickly as possible to keep out the butyric acid bacteria.
Lactic acid	Colour: bright light green to yellow-green. Smell: sharp and vinegary. Texture: firm, soft tissue not easily rubbed from fibres. Taste: sharply acid, pH 4 or less.	Good, and palatability should be excellent.	The lactic acid bacteria have dominated the ensiling process. They have grown rapidly to produce sufficient acid to keep out the spoiling bacteria. Dry conditions have favoured the lactic acid bacteria and if the ensiled crop has been young and leafy, an additive has been added to provide sugar or acid to stimulate the desirable bacteria.	Do not prevent, encourage!

Under *hot* fermentation methods the crop is allowed to warm up to 90–100°F (35°C), and it is then kept at that temperature. At this relatively high temperature few butyric bacteria can gain a foothold in the silo as they prefer lower temperatures, and therefore lactic acid silage should be produced.

With *cold* fermentation methods, provided the crop is wilted and dry, and additives are used to provide sugar or acid for the lactic bacteria, good silage can be made at lower temperatures (below 60°F (15°C) with no risk of butyric bacteria predominating. Furthermore, at this lower temperature, as there has been less breakdown of the carbohydrate, a more valuable silage is produced.

RULES FOR MAKING SILAGE

For both techniques it is absolutely essential to ensile the crop in as dry a condition as possible *if a high dry matter silage is to be produced.*

The silo should be filled with the middle kept slightly lower than the outsides, and particular attention must be paid to pressing the crop down at the sides. The sides of both clamp and stack silos should be raked down hard during the course of building. All these points will help to minimize side wastage. The crop should be ensiled carefully to reduce air pockets which would lead to mouldy silage. Tractor consolidation, and/or covering with a plastic sheet at night will reduce losses considerably.

As the silo nears completion it must be filled in the middle, and preferably the last few loads should be of a young and sappy type of crop. This, with the aid of thorough tractor consolidation, will help to get a good seal on top. The silo can then be covered if necessary with lime, plastic sheeting or corrugated iron, but if under a Dutch barn no cover will be needed.

With the hot fermentation method it is necessary to maintain a temperature of about 100°F (37°C) during the ensiling process. On occasions the temperature may fall well below 100°F, and then filling and consolidation should stop until the temperature rises again.

With the cold fermentation method it is important to keep the temperature below 60°F, (15°C); fast filling of the silo, together with thorough consolidation, is necessary. A dry crop is very essential. An additive, such as molasses, is sprayed on at the rate of 2–3 gal per ton of green material, or an acid supplement, such as calcium formate, applied at 5–6 lb per ton of green material, to provide ideal conditions for the lactic acid bacteria.

HAYLAGE AND DRILAGE

These terms are applied to green crops which are wilted in the field before being placed in an airtight tower silo as illustrated on p. 203). With haylage the crop is wilted down to a 50–60% moisture content, whilst with drilage the crop is wilted to 60–70% moisture content.

There should be very little wastage with these methods, and the material produced can have a much higher nutritive value than silage. But as wilted crops must be used some losses in the field will occur, and these can be considerable in wet weather.

The very high capital cost involved for the silo and other equipment will prevent the widespread use of this form of conservation.

VACUUM SILAGE

A recent development is the making of "vacuum" silage. The material to be ensiled is enclosed in polythene sheets which can be sealed by special plastic sealing strips. Air is extracted through a valve in the sheeting by a vacuum pump. This reduces respiration losses to a minimum and helps to consolidate the heap. A seepage valve can be fitted if required. Very high quality silage can be made by this method.

Suggestions for Classwork

(1) Identify the grasses and clovers of agricultural importance, both in their vegetative and flowering stage.
(2) Examine a seeds mixture, and identify the different types of seeds.

(3) Compare the periods of production of a ryegrass and non-ryegrass sward.

(4) Study and compare different techniques of grazing dairy cows and beef cattle.

(5) Study and compare different methods of fattening lambs off grass.

(6) Visit a barn hay-drying plant, and compare barn dried hay with that made in the field.

(7) Examine different samples of silage, and make notes on the type of fermentation, dry matter content and amount of wastage present in the silo.

CHAPTER 6

WEEDS

WEEDS are plants which are growing where they are not wanted.

Harmful Effects of Weeds

(1) Weeds reduce yields by shading and smothering crops.

(2) Weeds compete with crops for plant nutrients and water.

(3) Weeds can spoil the quality of a crop and so lower its value, e.g. wild onion bulbils in wheat; ryegrass in a meadow fescue seed crop.

(4) Weeds can act as host plants for various pests and diseases of crop plants, e.g. charlock is a host for flea-beetles and club-root which attack brassica crops: fat hen and knotgrass are hosts for virus yellows and root eelworm of sugar-beet.

(5) Weeds such as bindweed, cleavers and thistles can hinder cereal harvesting and increase the cost of drying the grain.

(6) Weeds such as thistles, buttercups, docks, ragwort, etc., can reduce the grazing area and feeding value of pastures. Some grassland weeds may taint milk when eaten by cows, e.g. buttercups, wild onion.

(7) Weeds such as ragwort, horsetails, nightshade, foxgloves and hemlock are poisonous and if eaten by stock are likely to cause unthriftiness or death. Fortunately, stock normally do not eat poisonous weeds.

Spread of Weeds

Weeds become established in various ways such as:

(1) *From seeds:*

    (a) sown with crop seeds—this is most likely where a farmer uses his own seed and it is not properly cleaned.

(b) shed in previous years; some weed seeds can remain dormant in the soil for up to 60 years.

(c) carried onto the field by birds and animals, or by the wind.

(d) in farmyard manure, e.g. docks and fat hen.

(2) *Vegetatively from:*

(a) pieces of *rhizomes* (underground stems), e.g. couch or twitch; creeping thistle, field bindweed and coltsfoot.
These pieces are usually carried about on field implements.

(b) pieces of *stolons* (surface runners), e.g. watergrass (bent grass).

(c) pieces of *roots*, e.g. docks and ragwort.

Control of Weeds

In recent years, the introduction of chemical *herbicides* or *weedicides* has greatly simplified the problem of controlling many weeds. Most of these chemicals can act in a *selective* manner by killing weeds growing is arable crops and grassland. The control of weeds with herbicides is now becoming an established and necessary practice on most farms. Nevertheless, it is worth remembering that other good husbandry methods can still play an important part in' controlling weeds.

Methods used to control weeds are:

(1) *Cultivations* (see p. 83).

(2) *Cutting*, e.g. bracken, rushes, ragwort, thistles. This weakens the plants and prevents seeding. The results are often disappointing.

(3) *Drainage.* This is a very important method of controlling weeds which can thrive in waterlogged soils. Lowering the water-table by good drainage will help to control weeds such as rushes, sedges and creeping buttercup.

(4) *Rotations.* By growing leys and various arable crops there is an opportunity of tackling weeds in many ways and at various times of the year. This method has become less important since herbicides were introduced.

(5) *Maintenance of good fertility.* Arable crops and good grass require a high level of fertility, i.e. the soil must be adequately supplied with lime, nitrogen, phosphates, potash and humus. Under these conditions crops can compete strongly with most weeds.

(6) *Chemical control.* It is outside the scope of this book to deal in detail with this very involved subject. However, the following is a summary of the main chemicals and methods which are used.

Most of the chemicals used have a *selective* effect, i.e. they are substances which stunt or kill weeds and have little or no harmful effects on the crop in which the weeds are growing. A severe check of weed growth is usually sufficient to prevent seeding and to allow the crop to grow away strongly.

Most of the common weeds found in cereals can now be controlled by selective herbicides. It is hoped, eventually, to have chemicals to control all weeds in all crops.

The *selectivity of a herbicide* depends on such factors as those summarized below:

(a) The *chemical* itself and its *formulation,* e.g. whether it is in water-soluble, emulsion or dust form; also whether wetters or spreaders have been added.

(b) The amount of the *active ingredient* applied and the quantity of carrier (water, oil or dust). Most herbicides are applied in water solution.

Volume rates for spraying	
Low vol.	5–20 gal/acre
Med. vol.	20–60 gal/acre
High vol.	60–100 gal/acre

(c) The *stage of growth* of the crop and the weeds. In general, weeds are easier to kill in the young stages of growth. However, treatment may have to be delayed until the crop is far enough advanced to be resistant to damage.

(d) *Weather* conditions. The action of some chemicals is reduced by cold air temperatures and rain after spraying.

The *chemicals now commonly used as herbicides* can be grouped as follows:

(1) *Contact herbicides*. These will kill most plant tissues with which they come in contact but they do not move through the plant. Shoots of perennial plants may be killed but regrowth from the underground parts usually occurs. Some examples of contact herbicides are *diquat, dinoseb, mineral oils, pentachlorophenol (PCP)* and *sulphuric acid*.

(2) *Residual herbicides*. When applied to the soil these chemicals persist for some time and kill weeds as they germinate. Some of these are selective, e.g. *simazine, atrazine, propham (IPC), endothal, linuron, prometryne* and *pryazon*.

(3) *Total herbicides*. These chemicals are used to kill all plant growth, e.g. on paths and other such areas. They are most effective on germinating seedlings, e.g. *simazine, atrazine, monuron, borax* and *sodium chlorate*.

(4) *Translocated herbicides*. This type of chemical moves about within the plant after being absorbed through the leaves or roots, e.g. *the "hormone" or "growth regulators"*; also *dalapon, amino-triazole* and *barban*.

(5) *The hormone (growth regulator) herbicides*. These are a special group of translocated chemicals which are similar to substances produced naturally by plants and which can regulate and control the growth of some plants. They are mostly used for controlling weeds in cereals and some can be used on grassland. The important ones are: MCPA, 2,4-D, CMPP, 2,4-DP, MCPB, 2,4-DB, MCPA/2,3,6-TBA and MCPA/dicamba.

Weed Control in Cereals

The commonest chemical which has been used on cereals is MCPA; 2,4-D has a similar effect but it is more likely to damage the cereals—especially oats.

The following common weeds are easily and cheaply controlled by MCPA (or 2,4-D):

Annual nettle	Fat hen	Poppy
Charlock	Fumitory	Runch
Corn buttercup	Hempnettle	Rush (common, soft)
Cornflower	Mustards	Shepherd's purse
Creeping buttercup	Orache	Thistles
Crowfoot	Pennycress	
Dock (seedlings)	Plantains	

If the cereal crop is *undersown with clover*, MCPB should be used to control all the above weeds except *hempnettle, runch* and *charlock*. To control these a little MCPA should be added to the MCPB.

Since the introduction of MCPA in 1942, several weeds, not controlled by MCPA, have become troublesome and may be controlled as shown in Table 18.

Mixtures of herbicides, which control many different kinds of weeds, are becoming more popular; some of these are patented.

Annual weeds are much easier to kill as seedlings. However, the safest time for spraying cereals is between the five-leaf and jointing stages of growth (see Fig. 75). There are exceptions to this, e.g. oats can be sprayed with MCPA after the first leaf stage and CMPP can be used after the three-leaf stage (see M.A.F.F. leaflet, STL/19).

Wild oats and *blackgrass* in wheat and some varieties of barley can be controlled by *barban*.

Couch (twitch) and other grass weeds can be controlled between cereal crops by spraying in the early autumn with *dalapon* and/or *amino-triazole*. Amino-triazole is also effective in controlling other weeds such as docks and creeping thistles.

Chemical Weed Control in Potatoes, Roots and Kale

Potatoes

Following limited, or no cultivations after planting, the field is sprayed with one or more chemicals when the first potato shoots appear. Various contact and residual chemicals can be used;

TABLE 18.

MCPA controlled weeds plus:	Straight cereals	Undersown with clover
Chickweed, cleavers.	CMPP (mecoprop)	Dinoseb
Black nightshade, chickweed, cleavers, campion, mayweeds, redshank, spurrey	MCPA/TBA ("18:15" mixture)	Dinoseb
Black bindweed, black nightshade, redshank	2,4-DP (dichlorprop)	2,4-DB/MCPA
Black bindweed, cleavers, chickweed, knotgrass, redshank	CMPP/, 2,4-D (mixture)	Dinoseb
The same, plus: black nightshade, campion, nipplewort and spurrey	MCPA/dicamba ("Banlene" mixture)	Dinoseb
Black bindweed, chickweeds, cleavers, knotgrass, mayweeds, corn marigold, redshank, scarlet pimpernel, speedwells	Ioxynil/CMPP or ioxynil/2,4-DP	Dinoseb/MCPA

Note. Dinoseb is very poisonous; protective clothing must be worn when using it.

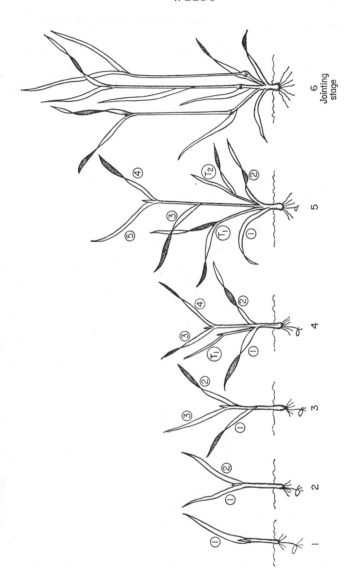

Fig. 75. Diagram to show the leaf stages in the cereal plant. T_1 and T_2 are tillers.

linuron plus *paraquat;* and *simazine* plus *prometryne* are promising mixtures now being used, but more research work is still necessary to find a control for some weeds, e.g. cleavers. Perennial weeds such as couch, creeping thistle and bindweed are not controlled in this way. Spraying with MCPA at a later stage of growth is likely to check the crop.

Sugar-beet

(a) Sugar-beet seedlings are slow in appearing above ground whereas most of the common weeds grow quickly. This means that the field can be sprayed with a contact chemical, e.g. PCP, to kill the seedling weeds just before the beet seedlings emerge.

(b) Wild oats can be usefully suppressed by several chemicals such as TCA, propham (IPC) and di-allate, worked into seed-bed before sowing.

(c) Many of the troublesome annual weeds can be controlled by band spraying (about 6 in. wide) at the time of sowing with chemicals such as "Murbetex" (endothal + propham) or "Pyramin" (pyrazon). They are not recommended for clays or black fen (peat) soils.

(d) Sodium nitrate ($2\frac{1}{2}$ cwt in 100 gal water/acre) plus wetter is sometimes used to control weeds when the beet plants are about the 3-leaf stage.

Kale

(a) A seed-bed can be prepared and left for the weeds to grow before sowing. These weeds can then be killed by a contact spray, e.g. *PCP* or *diquat,* and the kale sown in rows immediately afterwards with the minimum disturbance of the soil.

(b) *Gas liquor* at up to 550 gal/acre can be sprayed on an established crop of kale and weeds. This usually kills most of the weeds and will scorch and slightly check the kale, but it recovers—helped by the nitrogen in the gas liquor and good growing conditions.

(c) Fat hen has been one of the most troublesome weeds in kale—it can now be controlled by spraying the crop with *desmetryne*

("Semeron") after the kale has three true leaves. This chemical also controls many of the other weeds present.

Swedes: delayed seed-bed technique (see "Kale" (a)).
Mangolds and *fodder beet:* as for sugar-beet.
   (See also M.A.F.F. leaflet. STL. 29.)

Weed Control in Grassland

In arable crops, most damage is caused by annual weeds, but in established grassland biennial and perennial weeds cause most trouble. The presence of the weeds causes a *reduction in yield, nutrient quality* and *palatability* of the sward. Stock do not like grazing near buttercups, thistles and wild onions. Some weeds are *poisonous*, e.g. ragwort and horsetails, and some can *taint milk* if eaten e.g. buttercups and wild onion.

Weeds in grassland are encouraged by such factors as:

(a) *Bad drainage*, e.g. rushes, sedges, horsetails and creeping buttercup.
(b) *Shortage of lime*, e.g. poor grasses (bents), sorrels.
(c) *low fertility:* many weeds can live in conditions which are too poor for good types of grasses and clovers.
(d) *Poaching* (trampling in wet weather): the useful species are killed and weeds grow on the bare spaces.
(e) *Over-grazing:* this exhausts the productive species and allows poor, unpalatable plants such as bent, Yorkshire fog, thistles and ragwort to become established.
(f) *Continuous cutting* for hay encourages weeds such as soft brome, yellow rattle, knapweed and meadow barley grass.

Chemicals are a useful aid to controlling grassland weeds but should not be regarded as an alternative to good management.

The main chemicals used are MCPB and 2,4-DB—these do not harm the clovers. If clovers are abundant, and if resistant weeds such as ragwort are present, then MCPA or 2,4-D may be used as a much cheaper and more effective remedy.

Table 19 is a guide to the control of the more troublesome weeds:

TABLE 19.

Weed	Control
Bracken	Cut or crush the fronds (leaves) twice a year when they are almost fully opened. If possible, plough deep and crop with potatoes, rape or kale before re-seeding. Chemical control is unreliable at present. Rotavating about 10 in. deep chops up and destroys the rhizomes.
Buttercups	Spray with MCPA or MCPB. The bulbous buttercup is the most resistant type.
Daisies	Spray with 2,4-D or MCPA.
Docks	Seedlings and curled-leaved type—spray with MCPA or MCPB. Broad-leaved type—plough and take cleaning crop, e.g. kale. Grazing with sheep is helpful.
Horsetail	If possible, improve drainage. Spraying with MCPA or 2,4-D will kill aerial parts only and regrowth occurs—but if it is done 2–3 weeks before cutting, the hay crop should be safe for feeding.
Plantains	Spray with MCPA or MCPB. Avoid poaching.
Ragwort	Cut before buds develop, to prevent seeding. Spray with 2,4-D or MCPA before the flower buds appear. Grazing with sheep in winter is helpful.
Rushes	Improve drainage, if possible. Common or soft rush—spray with MCPA or 2,4-D. Hard and jointed rushes—cut several times per year. Encourage grasses and clovers by good management.
Sorrel	Spray with MCPA or 2,4-D. Apply lime.
Thistles	Spray with MCPA or MCPB. The more resistant creeping type should be sprayed in the early flower-bud stage. Avoid over-grazing.
Tussock grass	Improve drainage. Cut off the "tussocks" with flail harvester or topper.

WEED CONTROL WHEN RE-SEEDING

When re-seeding a grass sward, without a cover crop, weeds can be troublesome—especially annuals such as charlock and fat hen. These can be controlled by topping in the young stages with the mower.

If grassland has to be re-seeded and ploughing is not possible, spraying with *paraquat*, *dalapon*, or *amino-triazole* and possibly 2,4-D is very helpful for destroying the old sward.

Spraying with Herbicides

This is a skilled operation and should be carefully carried out. Some of the more important precautions to take are:

(1) Make a careful survey of the field to determine the weeds to be controlled and choose the most suitable chemical.

(2) Check carefully the amount of chemical to be applied per acre and the volume of water to be used (20–30 gal/acre is a common range). Make sure the chemical is thoroughly mixed with the water before starting. Soluble and wettable powders should be mixed with some water before adding to the tank. Use the agitator if necessary.

The rate of application is mainly controlled by the forward speed of the tractor (use a speedometer), and the size of nozzle, and to a lesser extent by the pressure (follow the maker's instructions). Always use clean, preferably not hard, water. Always use a filter. An accurate dipstick is necessary when re-filling the tank if it is not emptied each time.

(3) When using poisonous chemicals, e.g. dinoscb, PCP, it is necessary to wear fully protective clothing (read carefully the instructions issued with such chemicals). Do not blow out blocked nozzles.

(4) Do not spray on a windy day—especially with the hormone type of herbicides and if the spray is likely to blow onto susceptible crops or gardens. Keeping the boom as low as possible and using a plastic spray guard can be helpful; also using higher volume (larger droplets) is better than a very low volume mist for avoiding spray drift.

(5) Special types of sprayers using vibrating booms or vibrating nozzles reduce the risk of drift to a minimum.

(6) Make sure that the boom is level and that the spray cones or fans meet just above the level of the weeds to be controlled.

(7) Spray the headlands first; when spraying the rest of the field the drill rows in cereal crops are a useful guide. If using a wide boom it is advisable to use markers; avoid "misses" by slight overlapping.

(8) Wash out sprayer thoroughly on waste ground and leave full of clean water—this avoids scale forming inside the tank which is one of the commonest causes of blockages in the nozzles.

(9) Do not mix different herbicides and insecticides in the sprayer without seeking advice on the matter; only some can be mixed.

As an alternative to *overall* spraying, *band* spraying, is often used when applying herbicides to root crops, e.g. sugar-beet. A band about 6 in. wide is sprayed over each row of seeds; the weeds between the rows are controlled by cultivations. This is especially useful when expensive chemicals are being used.

Suggestions for Classwork

1. Examine seedlings of the common agricultural weeds in your area and learn how to identify them. Helpful pictures of weeds are published by the leading firms marketing herbicides.
2. When visiting farms make notes on the sprays used to control weeds, e.g. the main weeds, the chemicals used, time and methods of application.

CHAPTER 7

PESTS AND DISEASES OF FARM CROPS

PESTS are responsible for millions of pounds worth of damage to agricultural crops in this country every year. Before discussing the various methods used to control pests, it is important to understand something of their structure and general habits. Insects are *invertibrates* i.e. they belong to a group of animals which do not possess an internal skeleton. Their bodies are supported by a hard external covering called *chitin*. This is segmented so that the insect is able to move.

From the diagram of the external structure of an insect (see Fig. 76) it can be seen that the segments are grouped into three main parts:

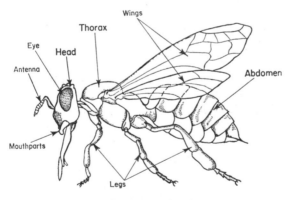

FIG. 76. Structure of an insect.

1. *The head*, on which is found:
    (a) The *antennae*—or feelers—for "smelling" and "tasting"

(b) The *eyes*—a number of single and compound eyes are present in most species.

(c) The *mouthparts* (see Fig. 77). Two main types are found in insects:

    (i) the biting type.

    (ii) the sucking type—insects in this group suck the sap from the plant and do not eat the foliage.

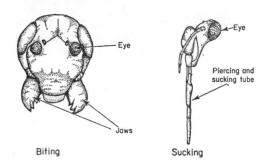

Biting   Sucking

FIG. 77. Insect mouthparts.

The type of mouthpart possessed by the insect is of considerable importance in deciding on the method of control.

2. *The thorax,* which bears:

(a) The *legs*—there are always three pairs of jointed legs on adult insects.

(b) The *wings*—found on most, but not on all, species.

3. The *abdomen,* which has no structures attached to it except in certain female species where the egg laying apparatus may protrude from the end.

Life-cycles

A knowledge of the life-cycles of insects can be of great help in deciding on the best stage at which the insects will be most susceptible to control methods.

Most insects begin life as a result of an egg having been laid by the female. What emerges from the egg, according to the species, may or may not look like the adult insect.

There are two main types of life-cycles:

(1) The "complete" or four-stage life-cycle (see Fig. 78).

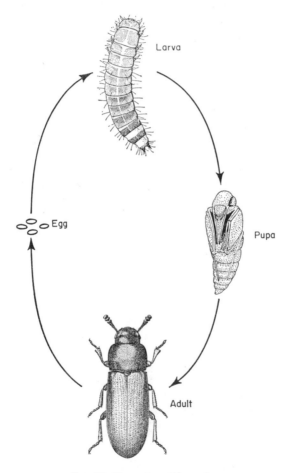

FIG. 78. Four-stage life-cycle.

(a) The *egg*.

(b) The *larva* (plural larvæ)—entirely different in appearance from the adult. This is the active eating and growing stage. The larvæ usually possess biting mouthparts, and it is at this stage with many insects that they are most destructive to crops on which they feed.

(c) The *pupa*—the resting stage. The larvæ pupate and undergo a complete change from which emerges—

(d) The *adult* insect—this feeds on crops but in many cases does far less damage than the larvæ.

(2) The "incomplete" or three-stage life-cycle (see Fig. 79).

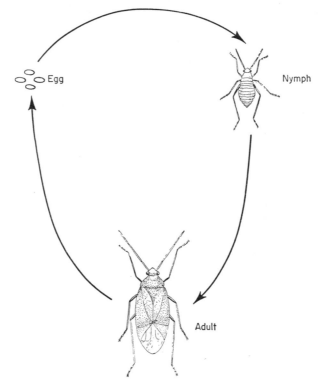

FIG. 79. Three-stage life-cycle.

(a) The *egg*.

(b) The *nymph*—this is very similar in appearance to the adult, although it is smaller and may not possess wings. It is the active eating and growing stage.

(c) The *adult* insect.

Most insects and/or larvæ and nymphs feeding on crops depend on these crops for part or all of their existence. The crop is the *host* plant, whilst the insect is the *parasite* to the host. Not all insects are parasitic; some are known as *predatory* insects in that they prey on other insects, killing and eating them. Some of these are beneficial to the farmer, e.g. the ladybird is particularly useful because, both as the larva and adult, it feeds on aphids which are responsible for transmitting certain virus diseases in plants.

Methods of Pest Control

1. INDIRECT CONTROL MEASURES

These aim more at the prevention of the pest attack.

(a) *Rotations*

As a means of control it is now not so important with more effective chemical control. The principal behind control by rotation is that if the host plant (the crop) is continually grown in the same field for too many successive years, then the parasite will increase in large numbers, e.g. eelworm.

(b) *Time of sowing*

(i) A crop may sometimes be sown early enough so that it can develop sufficiently to withstand an insect attack, e.g. frit fly.

(ii) A crop can be sown late enough to avoid the peak emergence of a pest, e.g. flea-beetle.

(c) *Cultivations*

Ploughing exposes pests such as wireworms, leatherjackets and caterpillars, which are then eaten by birds. Well prepared seedbeds encourage rapid germination and growth. This will often enable a crop to grow away from pest attack.

(d) *Encouragement of growth*

Good quality seed should be used which will germinate quickly and evenly. It is also important that the crop is not checked to any extent, say by lack of a plant food. A poor growing crop is far more vulnerable to pest attack than a quick growing crop. A top-dressing of nitrogen, just as a crop is being attacked, may sometimes save the crop.

(e) *Clean farming*

Weeds are alternate hosts to a great variety of insects, and, as far as possible, these sources of infestation should be eradicated.

2. BIOLOGICAL CONTROL

A parasite or predator is used to control the pest. The method has little application in this country.

3. DIRECT CONTROL MEASURES

This means chiefly chemical control using an insecticide. Insecticides can be used in a number of ways as:

> Sprays and dusts.
> Baits for controlling soil pests such as leatherjackets, slugs and snails.
> Seed dressing—mainly for the protection of cereals against wireworm and brassica crops against flea-beetle. Usually the insecticides are combined with a fungicide such as an organo-mercury compound.

Gases, smokes, fumigants are commonly used in greenhouses against aphids chiefly, and in granaries against beetles and weevils.

Basically, there are two ways in which insecticides kill insects:

(1) *By contact*

The insect is killed when it comes in contact with the chemical, either when:

(a) it is directly hit by the spray or dust,
(b) it picks up the insecticide as it moves over foliage which has been treated,
(c) it absorbs vapour from the insecticide,
(d) it passes through soil which has also been treated.

(2) *By ingestion*

As a *stomach* poison the insect eats the foliage treated with the insecticide, or the chemical is used in a bait. As a *systemic* insecticide it is applied to the foliage or to the soil around the base of the plant. It gets into the sap stream of the plant and thus the insect is poisoned when it subsequently sucks the sap.

Most insecticides kill by more than one method, which makes them very effective. But many of them are extremely toxic to animals and humans, and by law, certain precautions must be observed by the persons using them.

There are two main groups of insecticides:

(1) *The chlorinated hydrocarbons*

These insecticides are all stomach and contact poisons and the main ones are:

(a) *DDT*. This is generally the most useful insecticide. It controls a wide range of both agricultural and fruit crop pests. Most beetles, caterpillars and weevils are susceptible to DDT. It can be used as a spray and a dust.

(b) *BHC*. As a spray and dust it is used extensively on fruit crops and it controls, amongst other insects, aphids, caterpillars and weevils. It is also a useful soil insecticide for control of wireworm and leatherjackets, but it can taint some crops such as potatoes.

(c) *Aldrin*. This is best used as a soil insecticide. It controls wireworms, leatherjackets, cutworms and chafers without any risk of taint in subsequent crops. It is used as a dust or spray and as a seed dressing.

(d) *Dieldrin*. This is a particularly useful insecticide for controlling fly pests such as mangold fly, carrot fly and cabbage root fly. It is used as a dust or spray and as a seed dressing.

It is now recommended that both aldrin and dieldrin be restricted in their application because they are so persistent, and it is feared that their continued use may contaminate crops to a dangerous level.

Aldrin may still be used against wireworm in potatoes, but it must be applied separately and not compounded in fertilizers. Seed dressings containing aldrin and dieldrin may still be used (a) for winter wheat to control wheat bulb fly, (b) on rubbed and graded sugar-beet seed.

(2) *The organo-phosphorus compounds*

As a group, these insecticides are far more dangerous to use and they should be handled strictly in accordance with the manufacturer's instructions. Most of them are systemic in action, and they are usually applied as a spray.

The following are examples of the many organo-phosphorus insecticides on the market:

(a) *Parathion*. This is an insecticide which controls aphids and red spider mites on glasshouse crops and sugar-beet. It is also used against soil pests such as eelworms.

(b) *Demeton-methyl*. This is a widely-used systemic insecticide for most agricultural and horticultural crops, controlling aphids and red spider mites.

(c) *Dimethoate.* This compound is used for the control of aphids and other pests on sugar-beet and other crops.

Care in handling insecticides has already been mentioned. It is also important to remember that a certain interval must be observed between the last application of the insecticide and:

(1) harvesting edible crops,

(2) access of animals and poultry to treated areas.

With some insectides this interval is longer than others. This is another reason for very careful reading of the manufacturer's instructions.

Table 20 gives the main pests attacking farm crops, and their control.

Other Pests of Crops

BIRDS

Generally birds are more of a friend to farmers than a foe, although this will depend on the district and type of farming carried out. To the grassland farmer in the west, birds are not nearly the pest they are to the arable farmer in the Midlands and East Anglia. All birds in their lifetime will eat a considerable quantity of cereal seed, but most of them help the farmer by eating many insect pests and weed seeds, and the diet of some in addition includes mice, young rats and other rodents.

The *wood pigeon* certainly does far more harm than good. Not only does it eat cereal seed and grain of lodged crops, it also causes considerable damage to young and mature crops of peas and brassicas. The only effective ways of keeping this pest down are by properly organized pigeon shoots and nest destruction.

MAMMALS

Of the wild animals found in the countryside, those which cause most damage to crops are:

(1) *Rabbits* and *hares*—these can be very serious pests. They eat many growing crops—particularly young cereals. Organized

TABLE 20. PESTS AND THEIR CONTROL

Crop attacked	Pest	Description	Life-cycle	Symptoms of attack	Control	Notes
Cereals	*Adult:* Click-beetle. *Larva:* Wireworm	*Adult:* Brown, ¼–⅓ in. long. *Larva:* Growing to 1 in. long, yellow colour.	Larvæ hatch out during summer from eggs laid in the soil. They take 4–5 years to mature, and after pupation in the soil, the adult appears in early autumn.	Yellowing of foliage followed by disappearance of successive plants in a row. This is caused by wireworm moving down the row. Larvæ eat into the plants just below soil surface. They are usually found in the soil around the plants.	Good growing conditions to help the crop grow away from an attack. Wheat and oats more susceptible than barley; they should not be grown where the wireworm count is over 800,000 per acre. All seed should be dressed with gamma BHC at 2 oz/bushel.	Do not confuse wire-worm attack with other pests such as eelworm.
	Adult: Cranefly *Larva:* Leather-jacket	*Adult:* Is the "Daddy Longlegs". *Larva:* Leaden in colour, 1¼ in. long.	Eggs laid on grassland or weedy stubble in the autumn from which the larvæ soon emerge. They feed on the crop the following spring, pupating in the soil during the summer.	Crop dies away in patches, root and stem below ground having been eaten. Larvæ found in soil.	If possible, plough the field before August to prevent the eggs being laid. DDT can be applied as a low volume spray, or a Paris green and bran bait broadcast late in the evening. Aldrin may be used on DDT-sensitive varieties of barley.	
	Larva: Wheat bulb fly	*Larva:* Whitish-grey, ¼ in. long.	Eggs laid on bare soil in the autumn. Larvæ feed on the crop until following May. Pupation then follows either in the soil or plant.	Central shoot of plant turns yellow and dies in early spring. Larvæ found in root of plant.	If possible, avoid sowing wheat where the field has lain bare from late summer. Seed dressing using organo-mercury compound plus BHC or aldrin is as effective as any method so far tried.	Wheat is only attacked.

	Larva	Life history	Symptoms	Control	Crops affected
Frit fly	*Larva:* Whitish, ¼ in. long.	Three generations in the year, the most important being the first when in May eggs are laid on oats. The larvæ feed on the crop, pupating in the soil in late June.	In early summer the central shoot of the plant wilts, turns yellow and dies, but the outer leaves remain green.	Sow spring oats early, and try and get them past the 4-leaf stage as quickly as possible.	Oats are attacked more than the other cereals. Spring oats are particularly susceptible.
Gout fly	*Larva:* Legless, yellowish-white, ¼ in. long.	Two generations in the year, the most important being the first. Larva hatch and feed in plant.	Leaf sheath surrounding the ear is swollen and twisted. Poorly developed grain emerges.	Sow the crop early. Good growing conditions will help to keep it growing well.	Barley is chiefly affected.
Stem and bulb Eelworm	Too small to be seen without magnification, but the cyst stage (female containing hundreds of eggs) is just visible.	Live and breed in the plant. If plant dies, eelworms become dormant in dead tissue or soil, becoming active again when conditions are suitable.	Twisting and swelling, and in many cases death of the plant.	Rotation to starve out the eelworm. Clean seedbed. Cysts and worms can be carried on the seed.	Chiefly attacks oats. Eelworms are not insects.
Slugs and snails	Field slug lightish-brown in colour, about 1¼ in. long.	Wheat grain damaged by being eaten in the ground before it germinates. Young cereals can be completely grazed off by a severe autumn attack. Most active in moist and humid conditions.		Baits such as Paris green or metaldehyde and bran spread evenly over the field prior to drilling. Extra cultivations in preparing the seedbed help to check the pests.	Winter wheat chiefly attacked.

TABLE 20. Pests and their Control—*continued*

Crop attacked	Pest	Description	Life-cycle	Symptoms of attack	Control	Notes
Stored grain	Saw-toothed grain beetle	*Adult:* Dark brown, ⅒ in. long. *Larva:* White and flattened.	Eggs are laid on the stored grain; larvæ feed on the damaged grain. Pupation takes place in the grain or store.	The grain heats up rapidly; it becomes caked and mouldy. This is seen with the appearance of the beetles.	Disinfect all grain stores with DDT or BHC. Infested grain should be fumigated.	
	Grain weevil	*Adult:* Reddish-brown, about ⅒ in. long with an elongated snout.	During autumn the weevils bore into the stored grain to lay their eggs. The larvæ feed inside the grain where they also pupate.	Hollow grains. Sudden heating of the grain. Weevils found a few feet below the surface of stored grain.	See the saw-toothed grain beetle.	
Brassicæ (cabbage, kale, swedes, turnips)	Flea-beetle	A minute black beetle with a yellow stripe down each wing case.	Adults emerge from hibernation during late spring to feed on crops. Eggs are laid, but larvæ do little damage. Pupation takes place in the soil during the summer.	Very small round holes are eaten in the seed leaves of the plants.	Sow the crop either early or late, i.e. avoid April and May. Good growing conditions to get the crop quickly past the seed leaf stage. Seed dressing containing gamma BHC should be carried out. A dust or spray containing DDT or BHC can be applied as soon as the attack is noticed.	Sugar-beet, mangolds and cereal crops can be attacked on occasions.
	Leather jacket	See leatherjackets on cereals.		Young plants severed off at ground level. Roots can be severely damaged. Larvæ found in soil near the roots.	Spray with DDT, or can use a bait.	

Beans	Bean aphid	Very small oval body, black to green colour.	There are many generations in the year. In summer winged females feed on the crop; wingless generations are then produced which continue to feed. Eventually a winged generation flies to the spindle tree on which eggs are laid for overwintering.	On all summer host plants, colonies of black aphids are seen on the stem, leaves (especially the underside) and on the flowers. The plant wilts; it can become stunted and with a heavy infestation it may be killed.	An organo-phosphorus insecticide should be used when the aphids are first seen. This may have to be repeated at least once in the season.	It also attacks sugar-beet and mangolds.
Peas, Beans and other legumes	Pea and bean weevil, and striped pea weevil	*Adult:* Yellowish-brown with stripes of lighter brown, ¼ in. long. *Larva:* Legless, white with brown head.	During early spring eggs laid in the soil near plants. Larvæ feed on roots, whilst adults feed on leaves. Pupation takes place in the soil in mid-summer.	Seedling crops checked. U-shaped notches at the leaf margins.	Apply DDT either as a dust or spray when the attack is noticed.	
Mangolds sugar-beet fodder beet	Mangold fly	*Larva:* Yellow-white, legless, ¼ in. long.	White oval-shaped eggs are laid on the underside of leaves in May. Larvæ bore into the leaf tissue and after about 14 days they drop into the soil where they pupate.	Blistering of leaf which can become withered. Retarded growth and in extreme cases death of the plant.	Good growing conditions to help the crop pass an attack. Spraying carried out using an organo-phosphorus insecticide when more than 25 hatched larvæ or eggs are counted per plant in the 6-8-leaf stage.	

TABLE 20. PESTS AND THEIR CONTROL—*continued*

Crop attacked	Pest	Description	Life-cycle	Symptoms of attack	Control	Notes
Man-golds, Sugar beet, Fodder beet,	Aphids (black and green fly)	The green-fly (peach potato aphid) has a very small oval-shaped body of various shades of green to yellow.	During spring winged aphids migrate to the summer host crops. They move from one plant to another, thus transmitting the virus from an unhealthy to a healthy plant.	A severe infestation can cause the death of the plant, but chiefly it will mean a bad attack of Virus yellows, as both aphids are responsible for carrying the virus causing this disease.	As for the bean aphid.	
	Root eel-worms	Only cysts seen on the roots.	Live and breed on root tissues, dropping off into the soil where they can remain dormant for up to 10 years, hatching out and feeding when conditions become suitable.	Crop failing in patches. Plants which do survive are very stunted in growth.	See stem eelworm on cereals.	In some areas, by law, sugar-beet may only be grown 1 year in 4 or 5 in fields known to be badly affected. If necessary the soil can be tested for an eelworm count.
	Wireworm	See wireworm on cereals.		The roots of seedling plants are bitten off.	A seed dressing containing organo-mercury plus dieldrin.	

Potatoes	Peach potato aphid (greenfly)	See aphids on Mangolds, sugar-beet and fodder beet.	A bad infestation will check the growth of the plant, and potato virus diseases are spread.	Spraying seed crops with an organo-phosphorus insecticide will help to check the spread of virus disease by killing the aphids.
	Wireworm	See wireworm on cereals.	Maincrop tubers are riddled with tunnel-like holes.	Aldrin dust or spray should be applied to the soil before planting. Lift the crop in early September if possible.
	Root-eelworm	See eelworm on sugar-beet.	See eelworm on sugar-beet.	
	Slugs	See slugs on cereals.	Maincrop potatoes damaged by pests eating holes in the tubers.	No control method for potatoes as damage takes place after the crop has been planted.
Grass	Leather-jacket	See leatherjacket on cereals.	Grass dying off in patches, the roots having been eaten away. Larvæ found in the soil.	Spray with DDT or aldrin or use a bait.

shoots can control hares. Clearance of scrub and gassing are helpful in controlling rabbits.

(2) The *brown rat*, the worst pest of all, eats and damages growing and stored crops.

(3) *Mice*, another serious pest, damage many stored crops.

The local rodent officer will give advice on methods of extermination.

The harmless mammals, as far as crops are concerned, are:

The *badger* and *hedgehog*—these eat lots of insects, slugs, mice, etc.

The *fox*—kills rats and rabbits.

The *squirrel*—eats pigeon's eggs.

Plant Diseases

Although there are many causes of unhealthy crops, such as poor fertility and adverse weather conditions, the chief cause is disease.

Diseases, like pests, annually cause millions of pounds worth of damage and loss to the agricultural industry.

The four main agencies of disease are:

1. FUNGI

Fungi are plants, but they are different from flowering plants in that they do not possess chlorophyll, i.e. the green colouring matter of leaves which is essential for photosynthesis. Therefore, as they cannot manufacture their own carbohydrate, they obtain it from living or dead plants. Thus it is convenient to divide fungi into two main classes:

(a) *Parasitic*. These are dependent on the living host. They are responsible for causing many plant diseases.

(b) *Saprophytic*. These live in dead plants. They play an essential part in helping to break down plant remains into humus.

There are many thousands of different species of fungus, the majority of which are invisible to the naked eye.

A typical fungus is composed of long, thin filaments (made up of single cells) termed *hyphæ*. Collectively these are known as *mycelium*. It is through the mycelium that the fungus absorbs nutrients from its host.

With most parasitic fungi, the mycelium is enclosed within the host (only the reproductive parts protruding), although some fungi are only attached to the surface of the host.

Reproduction

Fungi can reproduce simply by fragments of the hyphæ dropping off, but usually reproduction is by *spores*. Spores can be compared to the seeds in ordinary plants, but they are microscopic and occur in immense numbers. The mycelium produces pods which contain the spores, and when the pod is ripe it bursts open, thus scattering the minute spores.

The dispersal of spores

It is important to understand how the spores are dispersed, and so infection spread from one plant to another. And knowing the particular form of dispersal will help in deciding disease prevention and control methods.

Spores can be dispersed by:

(i) *The Seed*. The disease is carried from one generation to the next by the spores attaching themselves to the seed, e.g. covered smut of cereals.

(ii) *The Soil*. The spores drop off the host plant and remain in the soil until another susceptible host crop is grown in the field. A suitable rotation will go a long way to check diseases caused in this manner, e.g. club-root of brassica.

(iii) *Wind*. Spores carried through the air can spread diseases from an unhealthy to a healthy plant, e.g. cereal smut and rust diseases.

Fungi do show great specialization in that they are only parasitic to one type of host plant or a closely related plant.

The extent of the disease caused by the fungi does depend upon soil and weather conditions and also upon the state of the host crop. A healthy crop which is growing well will withstand an attack far more successfully than a stunted, slow-growing crop.

2. VIRUSES

The discovery of the virus is very recent, and because it is so difficult to isolate little is known about it. It is a very small organism indeed. Something like one million viruses could be contained on an average bacterium. Only by using electron microscopes can it be seen that plant viruses have a sort of crystalline form.

All viruses are parasitic. They are not known to exist as saprophytes. But virus diseases differ from those caused by fungi and bacteria. The spread of the disease is rarely, if ever, passed through the seed.

The virus is present in every part of the infected plant except the seed. Therefore if part of that plant, other than the seed, is propagated, then the new plant is itself infected, e.g. the potato. The tuber is attached to the stem of the infected plant, and infection is carried forward when the tuber is planted as "seed".

With most plant virus diseases, the infection is transmitted from a diseased to a healthy plant by aphids. These are sucking insects which carry the infected sap.

3. BACTERIA

Bacteria are very small organisms, only visible under a microscope. They are of a variety of shapes, but those that cause plant diseases are all rod-shaped. Like fungi, bacteria feed on both live and dead material. Although they are responsible for many diseases of humans and livestock, in this country they are of minor importance compared with fungi and viruses as causal agents of crop diseases.

Bacteria reproduce themselves simply by the process of splitting into two. Under favourable conditions this division can take place every 30 minutes or so. Thus bacterial disease can spread very rapidly indeed, once established.

4. LACK OF ESSENTIAL PLANT FOODS (*Mineral Deficiency*)

When essential plant foods become unavailable to particular crops deficiency diseases will appear. Most of the diseases are associated with a lack of trace elements, but shortage of any essential plant food will certainly reduce the yield, cause stunted growth, and make the crop more vulnerable to pest and disease attack (see also "Chemical Elements Required by Plants", p. 27).

The Control of Plant Diseases

Before deciding on control measures it is important to know what is causing the disease. Having ascertained, as far as possible, the cause, the appropriate preventative or control measure can then be applied.

1. CROP ROTATIONS

A good crop rotation can help to avoid an accumulation of the parasite. In many cases the organism cannot exist except when living on the host. If the host plant is not present in the field, in a sense the parasite will be starved to death, but it should be remembered that:

(a) Some parasites take years to die, and they may have resting spores in the soil waiting for the susceptible crop to come along, e.g. club-root of the brassica family.

(b) Some parasites have more than one host, e.g. fungus causing black rust of wheat is a parasite on the barberry tree.

2. REMOVAL OF WEED HOST

Some parasites use weeds as alternative hosts. By controlling the weeds the parasite can be reduced, e.g. cruciferous weeds such as charlock are hosts to the fungus responsible for clubroot.

Both these preventative measures (1 and 2) illustrate the importance of having a sound knowledge of the parasites attacking crops.

3. CLEAN SEED

The seed must be free from disease. This applies particularly to wheat and barley which can carry the fungus causing loose smut deeply embedded in the grain. Seed should only be used from a disease-free crop.

With potatoes it is essential to obtain clean "seed", free from virus. In some districts where the aphid is very prevalent, potato seed may have to be bought every year.

4. RESISTANT VARIETIES

In plant breeding, although the breeding of resistant varieties is better understood, it is not by any means simple.

A new variety resistant to a certain disease may not be sufficiently heavy yielding to be worth growing; its quality may be poor and it may be susceptible to other diseases. Very often the resistance of a plant breaks down after a few generations, and new strains of the parasite may develop to which the plant shows no resistance.

But, in spite of all these difficulties, it would seem that in crop resistance lies the best solution to the control of plant disease.

5. THE CONTROL OF INSECTS

Some insects are carriers of parasites causing serious plant diseases, e.g. control of the green-fly (aphid) in sugar-beet will reduce the incidence of virus yellows. Furthermore, fungi can very often enter through plant wounds made by insects.

6. REMEDYING PLANT FOOD DEFICIENCIES

In many cases a deficiency disease can easily be overcome if the deficient plant food is remedied at an early stage.

7. THE USE OF CHEMICALS

Broadly speaking, chemical control of plant diseases means the use of a fungus killer—a fungicide. A fungicide may be applied to the seed, the growing plant, or to the soil. It can be used in the form of a spray, dust or gas. To be effective, it must in no way be harmful to the crop, nor after suitable precautions have been taken, to the operator or others, and it must certainly repay its cost.

The dressing of seed with a fungicide—seed disinfection

This is carried out to prevent certain soil and seed-borne diseases. In many cases an insecticide is added to help prevent attacks by soil-borne pests. Various fungicides can be used, depending upon the disease to be controlled:

(a) *The organo-mercury.* They are used as a preventative measure against soil and seed-borne diseases of cereals, sugar-beet, fodder beet and mangolds. These compounds are available in the dry and liquid forms.

(b) *Thiram.* This is used as a dry seed dressing to prevent seed decay and pre-emergence damping-off in peas and other vegetables.

The composition of these fungicides will vary slightly according to the particular commercial brand, but they are all approximately the same, consisting of a very small percentage of the actual poison, plus a large percentage of the carrier. A dye is added so that dressed seed can easily be distinguished. The dressing of seed is preferably carried out by a seeds merchant. There should be very little extra charge.

Treated seed should be sown as soon as possible, but if temporary storage is necessary it should be kept in dry, airy conditions. It should not be used for human or animal consumption.

Application to the plant

A good example is the control of potato blight. The fungicide can be used as a dust or spray, and it may have to be repeated at 10–14-day intervals, according to the season.

Copper, in various forms, or more recently, *zinc* compounds, are the chemicals used for controlling blight.

Soil use of fungicides

Has little application in agriculture.

Table 21 gives the main plant diseases affecting farm crops, and their control.

TABLE 21. PLANT DISEASES AND THEIR CONTROL.

Crop attacked	Disease	Causal agent	Symptoms of attack	Life-cycle	Methods of control
Cereals	(1) Bunt, covered or stinking smut of wheat (2) Covered Smut of Barley (3) Covered and loose smut of oats	Fungus	Brown or black spore bodies instead of grain in the ears.	Infected grain is planted; seed and fungus germinate together and thus young shoots become infected. The spores are released when the skin breaks, and so combining or threshing contaminates healthy grain.	Organo-mercury seed dressing at 1–2 oz per bushel of seed. It is unwise to dress seed with a moisture content of more than 16%.
	(1) Leaf stripe of barley (2) Leaf stripe of oats	Fungus	The first leaves have narrow brown streaks. Subsequently brown spots appear on the upper leaves.	Infected grain is planted; seed and fungus germinate together and thus young shoots are infected. From the secondary infection, spores are carried to the developing grain.	As for the covered smuts.
	(1) Loose smut of wheat (2) Loose smut of barley	Fungus	Infected ears a mass of black spores. They do not remain enclosed within the grain as with the covered smuts.	Similar to the covered smuts, but the fungus develops within the grain. The spores are dispersed by the wind to affect healthy ears.	(1) Resistant varieties. (2) Clean seed. (3) Hot water treatment of suspected infected grain. A skilled operation, not done by the farmer.
	Yellow rust	Fungus	Yellow coloured pustules in parallel lines on the leaves, spreading in some cases to the stems and ears. In a severe attack the foliage withers and shrivelled grain results.	The fungus mainly attacks wheat. Infection appears on the plant from May onwards. From the pustules, spores are carried by the wind to infect healthy plants. During winter, spores are dormant on autumn sown crops.	Resistant varieties.

				Resistant varieties.
Black stem rust or Black Rust	Fungus	Reddish-brown lines or spots on the leaves and stems, later succeeded by black streaks on the foliage.	Spores are wind-borne—often over long distances—from barberry bushes and then from plant to plant. It does most damage on wheat in south-west counties.	Spring sown barley and wheat are more resistant than autumn sown crops. Arrange a break of at least 2 years from cereals. Cappelle and Maris Widgeon (winter wheats) show good resistance.
Eyespot (sharp eyespot is similar but not so serious)	Fungus	Eye-like lesions on stem about 3 in. above ground. Grey "mould" inside stem; straws lodged in all directions. No darkening at base of stem.	The fungus can remain in the soil, on old stubble and some species of grasses for several years. It usually attacks susceptible crops in the young stages.	Rotation to starve the fungus.
Take-all or whiteheads	Fungus	Black discoloration at base of stem. Grey colour of roots. Ease with which plant can be pulled from the soil. Infected plants ripen prematurely, and produce bleached ears containing little or no grain.	Wheat and barley only affected. The fungus survives in the soil in root and stubble residues and the host plant is infected when it is grown in the field.	
Brassicas (cabbage, kale, swedes and turnips) Club root or finger and toe	Fungus	Swelling and distortion of the roots. Stunted growth. Leaves pale green in colour.	A soil-borne fungus. The fungus grows in the plant roots and causes the typical swellings. Resting spores can pass into the soil especially if diseased roots are not removed. They can remain alive for several years, becoming active when the host crop is again grown in the field.	(1) *Rotation.* With a bad attack advisable not to grow the crop for at least 5 years in the field. (2) *Liming and drainage.* The spores are more active in acid and wet conditions. (3) *Resistant crops.* Kale is more resistant than swedes or turnips. Some varieties of swedes and turnips are more resistant than others.

TABLE 21. PLANT DISEASES AND THEIR CONTROL—*continued*

Crop attacked	Disease	Causal agent	Symptoms of attack	Life-cycle	Methods of control
Brassicas	Brown heart of swedes	Boron deficiency	No external symptoms, but when the root is cut open a browning or mottling of the flesh is seen. Affected roots are unpalatable.		See heart rot of sugar-beets.
Peas	(1) Pre-emergence damping-off	Fungi and bacteria	(1) The seeds and young seedlings rot before the shoots emerge above ground.	The organisms are soil-borne. They feed on the young plants when grown in the field, and return to the soil on the death of the plant.	Seed dressing using thiram. This has the effect of increasing the percentage emergence and stand of seedlings.
	(2) Foot-rots		(2) Base of stems of young plants blackened.		
Sugar-beet, mangolds, fodder-beet	Virus yellows	Virus	First seen in June/early July on single plants scattered throughout the crop—a yellowing of the tips of the plant leaves. This gradually spreads over all but the youngest leaves. Infected leaves thicken and become brittle. The yield is seriously reduced by an early attack.	The crop is infected by aphids which have overwintered in mangold clamps and steckling beds. The aphids carry the virus, and they can very quickly infect the whole crop.	(1) Good growing conditions to keep the crop growing vigorously. (2) All mangold clamps should be cleared by the end of March. If not, they should be sprayed to kill any aphids. (3) Seed crop stecklings should not be raised in the main sugar-beet areas. (4) An organo-phosphorus insecticide should be used when the aphids are first seen. This may have to be repeated at least once.

			Symptoms		
	Heart rot	Boron deficiency	In young plants the youngest leaves turn a blackish-brown colour and die off. A dry rot attacks the root and spreads from the crown downwards. The growing point is killed, being replaced by a mass of small, deformed leaves.		This deficiency is more apparent on dry and light soils and can be made worse by heavy liming. Apply borax at 20 lb/acre as soon as the disease is seen. Use a boronated compound fertilizer on suspected soils.
Potatoes	Blight	Fungus	Brown areas on leaves. Whitish mould on the underside of leaves. Leaves and stems become brown and die off.	Infected tubers (either planted, ground keepers, or throw outs from clamps) produce blighted shoots. From these shoots the fungus spores are carried by the wind to infect the haulms. From the haulms the spores are washed into the soil to infect the tubers. Infection can also take place at harvest.	The disease is very dependent on the weather. Beaumont warnings can be given to growers by the Advisory Service. These indicate when conditions are most favourable to blight infection. 10/14 days' warning of outbreaks are possible, and the grower is then advised to spray or dust his crop. An early preventative application before there is any sign of attack should be given using copper or zinc compounds. Before harvesting, the haulm should be chemically destroyed to lessen the risk of tubers becoming infected as they are lifted.

TABLE 21. PLANT DISEASES AND THEIR CONTROL—*continued*

Crop attacked	Disease	Causal agent	Symptoms of attack	Life-cycle	Methods of control
Potatoes	Leaf roll	Virus	Lower leaves are rolled upwards and inwards; they feel brittle and crackle when handled. The other leaves are lighter green and more erect than normal. Yield is lowered.	The virus is transmitted by aphids from plant to plant. Infected tubers (which show no sign of the disease) are planted and thus the disease is carried forward from year to year.	(1) Use certified "seed" which is grown in areas such as Scotland and Northern Ireland where aphids are not prevalent due to the colder climate. Thus the "seed" is free from virus infection. (2) Systemic sprays will control the aphids, and thus reduce the spread of virus.
	Dry rot	Fungus	Infected tubers are usually first noticed in January and February. The tuber shrinks and the skin wrinkles in concentric circles. Blue-pink or white pustules appear on the surface.	The soil-borne fungus enters the tuber from adhering soil. Infection can only enter through wounds and bruises caused by rough handling at harvest. The disease can be easily spread during storage.	(1) If the potatoes are handled carefully, infection is considerably reduced. Some varieties are more resistant than others to the disease. (2) Dust the seed with tetrachlornitrobenzene when storing.

Suggestions for Classwork

1. Make a collection of the most important pests attacking crops.
2. Look out for any possible pest and disease attack on crops growing in the district. Examine closely the symptoms of attack, and find out the most suitable remedy.
3. When handling insecticides and fungicides, pay every attention to the manufacturers' instructions.

INDEX